Memoirs of a Taxi Driver

Memoirs of a Taxi Driver

C. E. Patterson

Trueblood Publishing
P.O. Box 806303
Chicago, IL. 60680

ISBN 0-9715252-0-X
LCCN 2001127192

Trueblood books are available at special discounts for bulk purchase for sales promotions, premiums, fund-raising, or educational use. For details, contact:

Trueblood Publishing
P.O. Box 806303
Chicago, Il. 60680

Printed In the United States of America

To My Mother, I Will Never Forget

Acknowledgements

I would like to thank Benjamin Franklin for writing: "They that can give up essential liberty to obtain a little temporary safety deserve neither liberty nor safety."

--Historical Review of Pennsylvania

I would like to thank the person that said: "Think for yourself, and always question authority."

--Unknown

Last, but not least, I would like to thank Bobbi for her untiring encouragement in my endeavor to finish this work.

Contents

Introduction

My parents are from the South, and their parents were sharecroppers in Alabama. Both of my grandparents' grandmothers were full-blooded Cherokee Indians.

I remember my mother telling me that when her mother's grandmother was near death, she told her mother to go out and get some wood from the woodpile. She went to get the wood as commanded, and when she returned, her grandmother was dead in the bed.

I sometimes wonder how they looked back then. They were too poor to have cameras. I don't know much about my grandparents, but my grandmother did looked like an Indian. Those Indian features were full and true in her face. She was a small woman, petite if you would see her now. If you could see my mother now, if you looked closely at her, you could see the Cherokee in her.

My grandfather was half white. You could say that. You could see the whiteness in him. My mother told me that he never left them, but he was not a kind person. He was not playful with them as other fathers were to their children. He never had time for them and would shoo them away.

When I first met my grandfather there was no affectionate embrace. I can't remember him coming to the door to greet us on our late night arrival. I cannot even remember him saying anything to me. He only sat in his rocking chair and

Introduction

talked to himself while looking out the window. I was glad the trip was over though. It was hot and humid on our arrival. I had never been to the South, and I was only thirteen years old then. Sitting in one place for hours was too much for me.

When my uncle drove us down there, I can't remember him turning on the air conditioner in the car, and when the trip was finally over, I was happy. Thinking carefully now, there was no air-conditioning in that car he drove us in that summer.

My grandparents lived in a white paneled house on the outside of Tuckersville. They were tucked in between other houses that were lined up along a red gravel road and red dust raised itself from the gravel whenever a car drove down it on a hot summer day.

After we had settled down for a few days, my uncle started to paint my grandparents' house. When he was not painting, he drove us out to the farm he grew up on. There was no farmhouse there when we got there. There was nothing there but the tree that once shielded their house from the sun with corn growing all around it.

The South is a quiet place. When I was down there, I had no trouble with the people. I even walked to town on my own and bought something from a small drug store. I walked around the town, and it was very quiet. My uncle told me the black people and white people knew each other. They knew theirs limits amongst themselves. After all, they had been living together for hundreds of years down in the South.

Nobody wants to be around black people. I remember as an adult I watched a program on television about a beauty pageant that was filmed in Alabama. The female contestants were second generation Indians from India. They did a day-to-day documentary on six contestants that had a very good chance of winning the beauty pageant. They interviewed friends, neighbors, and classmates. They even visited mosques and Hindu temples where those people

3

worshipped. One Indian family that participated in the beauty pageant was Southern Baptist. The camera was everywhere following those contestants, and not one had an African-American friend or associate. It was so sad. As a matter-of-fact, some of those Indians were darker than many African-Americans.

When I was seventeen, my uncle took my brother and I back down to the South with him again. My uncle painted the house again, and the rest of us just sat around. I was not bored in the least. There were chickens and even a goat in the yard, and my grandmother was a good cook. My grandmother is dead now. I wish now I could have asked more questions of her. She was living history in front of me, and I did nothing with it. Well, I was only seventeen then. I knew nothing then. I had more important things to contemplate.

My uncle brought some of his children with him on that trip to the South. When my uncle took us back to Chicago, he left my older brother with my grandparents, and I went back north with my uncle. I was tempted to stay myself for the summer, but I wanted to come back home. I remember my brother standing on the veranda with my grandmother. I felt inside we should not be leaving him; I felt sorry about leaving him. But now I wish it had been me. I lost that important time with my grandparents; they are both dead, and all that history is gone from me.

When my uncle went back down at the end of the summer to retrieve my brother, my brother came back needing a haircut. His facial countenance looked wild, and the sun had made his skin black and smooth like a chocolate bar. It felt to me that he had been gone a long time. I asked him many questions about what had happened down there. But to this day I cannot remember a thing he told me.

THAT STORY WAS TOLD to me by a cab driver named Mitchell Goodboy, a man in his early sixties. He had lived in Chicago all of his life, and what was so unusual about

Introduction

him was that he had graduated from a major university after receiving a baccalaureate in psychology at twenty-three-years old. I, myself, was studying journalism at that same university he had graduated from. I had just gotten married and was driving a taxi on summer vacation to earn extra money to continue my education when I met him.

I met Mr. Goodboy one night at the staging area at the airport. While standing there in line with the other drivers, pushing the taxis ahead of us with our hopes and wishes, I saw a man quite well groomed with a slightly graying beard sitting patiently smoking his pipe. I could not help approaching that man and questioning him. He neither looked like a cab driver nor behaved like a cab driver.

I told him that he did not look like a cab driver or behaved like one; he removed his pipe from his mouth and told me he was indeed a taxi driver.

I asked how he had come into his vocation, and he told me he had worked for a marketing firm in his twenties, studied some law after graduating from college but found that he had spent the money unwisely. Taxi driving he said was profitable, relaxing, and rewarding if you knew how to work the business.

After I had started driving a cab, I found myself discussing with any cab driver I might meet at a cabstand or at the airport their experiences as a cab driver, their backgrounds, hopes, and dreams for the future. I found that most taxi drivers are only part-time drivers, and only a few are full-time professionals. All taxi drivers who are professionals find it rewarding financially and even raise families with their income. The taxi drivers I have met are very intelligent and are almost always foreign born.

Almost all foreign-born taxi drivers speak English with a foreign accent. Because English is not their first language, they find it difficult to discourse in English and are starved for relaxed conversation. They all have stories to tell and have a sense of wisdom that is profound to those who might listen.

Memoirs of a Taxi Driver

That short talk I had with Mr. Goodboy interested me in him more than any other cab drivers I had met prior to him. He was educated, had mastered the English language excellently, was very descriptive in his experiences, a very good storyteller, incorporated drama into his stories, and chose his words very carefully.

I told him that I had secured a part-time job for the fall semester with a major publication and that I was collecting material for a story or novel I might do in the future about my experiences with cab drivers and driving a cab in the city. He agreed to let me interview him, and I brought my tape recorder to his apartment on his days off. An interview that I thought would last only a summer actually lasted a year. My interviews with Mr. Goodboy showed me a side of the cab business a summer of driving could never teach me. "With My Strong Hand" is one of the selected stories in this publication told to me by Mr. Goodboy. I set in front of him with my ears and eyes open as a child listening to his father tell him a bedtime story.

The cab driver in a community can come from any class of society. Mr. Goodboy I found out was a product of an urban middle-class family. He lived not far from the city center in a three-bedroom apartment, in a building that he had lived in over thirty-five-years. He had no wife or children. When I asked him why he had such a large apartment for a bachelor, I was told that besides a bedroom for himself, he kept an office in one bedroom and the other bedroom he kept for storage.

He is a tall slender man with a full head of gray hair, a nicely trimmed graying beard, and a trim waist for a man in his sixties. Besides smoking a tobacco pipe, he neither smokes cigarettes or drinks alcohol.

He is a very neat man. Every piece of furniture and fixture is in its place, and there is almost no dust about the apartment. To see if his neatness was because of my expected visit, I asked him to give me a tour of his apartment. When that tour ended, I found nothing in his

Introduction

apartment disorganized. I asked him to open a closet at random to look into, and even that closet was organized with its contents as neatly placed as artifacts in a museum display. That made me think of my closets at home, and I made a commitment then and there to do something about them when I left Mr. Goodboy's home.

When we set down to talk, he did not reach for his pipe but leaned back in a recliner, looking not like a cab driver, but an attorney, doctor or one fortune 500 CEO. When he started, he started without a stutter or hesitation.

--Darius Mionskowski, October 1999.

Prologue

Place your microphone close to me so that your readers can hear my story clear in their minds.

I know that what I am about to tell you will be boring to listen to. It is all about me, and my unimportant life. But if you listen to me, understand me, you will understand the stories that I will tell you in the weeks to come. Be patient with me if you will, and you will understand.

I am a taxi driver. I have been one almost all my adult life. It is clear in my mind today how I started to drive a taxi. It is a good business to be in. You make copious amounts of money, get to see the city, and you get to make love to a lot of female passengers if you play your cards right. Sometimes, you can even fall in love with one of those women.

The reason I tell you this is because the multitude of people who get into taxis and walk pass them everyday are not aware of that truth. It is a business I would recommend to anyone who would need extra money in the pocket. I would recommend it to anyone who needs excitement, adventure, and wisdom in their lives.

I was born here. I was born in this city. I was about five years old when I started to remember events that are in my mind even today. I lived with my mother and father in a small house not far from where I sit now. I remember it as an attractive domicile. At my age our house appeared to be the best looking house on the block. That is what I remember first, how attractive our house was. I remember when my mother went to work we had a baby sitter that took care of us.

I remember one in particular that was very kind to us. She was an older woman who dressed us up in old clothing and let us run throughout the house. Her name was Hattie. I can remember her heartsome personality in our living room at this moment.

When she came to baby-sit with us, she would sometimes bring food from her house to eat. She brought canned preserves that tasted delicious. I cannot remember how she looked, her face, but she was very good, and even now that I am in my sixties; I can still remember her name and kindness.

What happened to her I do not remember. One day I remember her gone from our lives.

We had other baby sitters who were not as pleasant or kind to us. I remember one who would go into the refrigerator and eat the food that my mother would buy for us. I would stand in the living room and watch as she hid herself from me with the refrigerator door. I would say to my older brother while pointing at her, "Jeffery, Jeffery, she's eating all our food. I am going to tell Mama when she comes home. You watch; I'm going to tell Mama." When my mother came home I would say, "Hey Mama, that girl, she ate all our food up while you were gone." I remember telling my mother that several times on her advent from work. Those revelations must have had an adverse impact on the girl's job, because I cannot remember her staying around very long.

I cannot remember the kind of work my father did to make a living at that time, but I do remember him taking us to movies on some Sunday nights while my mother was at

Memoirs of a Taxi Driver

church. I cannot remember the movie or the movie theater, but I remember my mother telling him that we had just had baths and we might catch cold. My mother was the enemy I felt. I wanted to go to the movies with my father, and she was stopping that.

I know inside of me that I was my father's favorite child. He was always placid towards me, holding me, and petting me. He accommodated my wishes often. It seemed he would always take me with him when he went places. I remember one Mother's Day he took my older brother and I out to buy a Mother's Day present for my mother. We went out and bought some ice cream and cookies and some soda pop. I was too young to realize he had bought those things for us. When we got home, I ran up to my mother and said, "Mama, Mama we bought you a Mother's Day present. Look, look Mama; we have ice cream and cookies." Those were good times for us.

My mother would let us go outside and play in front of the house on occasion. We were specifically told not to go around the corner from in front of the house. I would want to stay in front of the house, but that was intractable for me, there was always something enticing about going around the corner. I would go around that corner, and when my mother did not see me in front of the house, I had to go back inside on punishment for not obeying her orders. I could not understand why I could not leave from the front of the house. My mother was the enemy.

On several occasions my mother had to leave us alone at home. That is the time I have my first remembrance of my younger sister. She was a tiny baby, and my mother always told me she was the loveliest of her children. She told me many times how a man walked up to her on the street while she had Cookie in her arms and took a picture of her. But my mother would leave us alone. That could have been the first time in their marriage that my mother and father were having spousal problems.

Prologue

We were at home, and we would play with the telephone while my mother was gone. We would say bad things to the operator. I am too embarrassed to say what we said on the telephone to the people who picked up at the other end.

I remember once we where on the telephone insulting the operator and hanging up the telephone on her, when, in a few minutes, the telephone rang and I picked it up. The voice on the other end of the telephone said, "When your mother gets back home, I'm going to call and tell her what you have been doing. If you pick up this telephone and call me one more time, I'm calling the police." The lady at the other end then hung up the telephone, and we never played with the telephone again. All that day Jeff and me were worried that our mother was going to find out about our licentious behavior. But she never did find out.

When I first started school, my older bother went to a private school across the street from our house, and I went to a public school down the block from our house. I would see him at a distance and point him out to my mother, "Mama, hey Mama, there's Jeff, see Mama, see Jeff. I see him Mama; I see Jeff." We would continue walking towards my school. On my first day I cried. I did not want my mother to leave me. It was a strange place, and I did not want to be there. But in time I became acquainted with my classmates, and after a few trips to school with my mother, I knew my way to school, and I would run through the wind not to be late. The school is not far from where we sit now. A new school has been built on that site now. The one I went to they demolished a long time ago.

I was a rambunctious boy in school. I was absolutely mean. I remember my mother had to go to my school because of my behavior. She took me home one day--I remember that walk home. She walked fast, holding my hand as we went. She beat me until the sun did not shine. "Boy you listen to me now. You are not going to be acting like that in school. You go there to learn, you don't go there to fight with other children. When your teacher tells you to

11

do something, you do it. You embarrass me. You wait until your father gets home, he's going to whip your behind good."

I cried, cried, and cried a long time before my father came home.

"Mama, I didn't do anything wrong, that teacher is mean to me. She can't teach. I hate her. I want to kill her. I'm never going back to that school again. I hate that school."

When my father came home he did not hit me and he said, "Listen to me little boy, you are going to go to school and learn. The school is not a place to fight other children. Don't you know they can put you in jail for fighting? You do as your teacher tells you. Your mother doesn't have the time to go to school every time you act up. If we get a letter from your teacher again, your behind is going to be so that you can't sit down on it when I finish with it." They did not take any hogwash from me. My conduct at school ameliorated after that.

I was not six years old when we moved from my mother and father's first house. The city condemned our house to build some housing projects, and we moved to a rented apartment behind a storefront. We lived there for a few months until my mother and father bought another house in the city. It was there that I lived until I graduated from high school. Soon after I graduated from high school, I entered the university. Before I left home I rented my first apartment, and I got a job in a restaurant as a waiter. When I moved, I moved gradually. Before they knew it, I was gone from the house and never went back. Like all boys in their minds, they think that their parents are too overbearing, and I was not different in my thinking than other boys my age.

It was time to get some girls in that new apartment of mine.

So, I moved away from home, rented my own apartment, but women were few in my life. I had no car to transport females in at that time. But I had money, because I had no

Prologue

expenses, I had money in my pockets. At the end of the week I always had a surplus of cash, but I had no private transportation. I asked my father to help me buy a car, and he did assist me in purchasing a vehicle. I was only nineteen at the time and could not sign a contract. I drove that car, and I had more women than I could handle, I had more sex than I could handle, I accumulated a large number of parking tickets, and I eventually had no money after that. I had the apartment, I had the women, I had all the good things that came with a car, but I was flat broke. No money, no women. That is when I started having trouble with my tuition payments.

Even though I had a job and my own apartment, I was a descent student. I was persistent. I studied when I was supposed to, and I passed my examinations. However, it would have been easier for me financially if I had stayed at home with my parents while I was attending college. My mother knew it was hard on me, and always said, "You are always welcome home honey." I did not want to go back home though. I wanted to make it on my own. I had my whole future in front of me.

When my funds ran low, I decided to take a semester off to accumulate some funds to continue my education. I worked two jobs as a waiter in restaurants, one during lunch and one during dinner. It was profitable. I started the following semester as I had planned. But my finances deteriorated to the point that I had to take another semester off to accumulate even more funds, and I still got a little behind on my tuition payments and could not continue. I had to sell my car and in that way I restarted.

I told a classmate that I had to sell my vehicle to find the funds to pay my tuition, and I had no transportation to get around the city. He told me that he drove a taxi part-time. He said it would behoove my situation if I leased a taxi and drove it when I needed a car to take care of errands that I might have to take care of that I could not do successfully without a motor vehicle.

Memoirs of a Taxi Driver

That was a splendid idea, and in those days it only took a few hours to get a chauffeurs license, and that is exactly what I did. I attained my license and drove a taxi only when I needed one. I met interesting people, and the money was excellent.

I transport people from all over the world. Some customers do not have the money on occasion, but Mexicans and those people from the countries that are south of Mexico always have the money and do not try to rob the taxi driver. I pick up a great number of Mexicans and Guatemalans. Many Mexicans and Guatemalans look like American Indians, but they will never confess that they have American Indian ancestry. It is embarrassing for Mexicans to have it known that Indian ancestry is in their blood.

One afternoon I picked up a beautiful woman who was heavily endowed with Indian ancestry. She was not tall and told me she was a mother in route to pick up her child. I asked politely if she had American Indian ancestry, and she did not acknowledge that she had any American Indian ancestry but mention her Spanish ancestry. I heard her not answer my question, and I inquired again about her ancestry and she expertly avoided the question, but I did not let her go free from my question and mentioned that she looked like an American Indian. She cleverly avoided my inquiry, and I was much more concise and asked, "Tell me the truth, you do have Indian ancestry, you skin is red, be truthful, it is only you and me here." She denied without saying that she had no Indian ancestry. To confirm that stigma of having Indian ancestry, I have asked many people from that part of the world about that concern. They have either denied or revealed that it is not a good idea to confess having American Indian ancestry. It just is not a good idea I have been told.

People deny a lot of things to themselves. I cannot deny that I think about my life now. I think about how I could have made my life better. I think about the relationships I

Prologue

have had with lovers and people in general. Sometimes I have sat at home for five and six hours, without moving, thinking about how my life could have been better.

Sometimes I will get up in the middle of the night and walk the streets without people being on them. How my mind started to think that way, I cannot precisely remember. But it did start, and ever since I have had that desire to be out in the night, not so much as to be out in some neighborhood venue, but in the business district of the city I live in. I have asked myself if it could have been an impulse that I received as a child as I delivered newspapers in the tall conical high-rises in the city center district or just some innate desire to be out in the darkness with the buildings towering over me. I say towering because they are towering, so tall, so big. I find myself peeping at their tallness often in admiration against the night sky. I get even more satisfaction when I am at the small airport on the lake, watching the planes take off and land there in the night. Even in the winter I have been known to sit there and watch those planes come and go.

In the morning as a boy, delivering newspapers in the city center of this large city, I would see men walking about the streets, who appeared to me not to have much money and little to do. They harmed me not, but stood about with their minds thronged in confusion. When they stood in a place, their bodies would spiral about from the alcohol, and when they would commence their perambulating, they did it not in a straight line.

I would sometimes see one or two of them working together at a fountain in a plaza collecting coins that had been thrown in some time earlier. One of the culprits would stand at the street corner as a lookout for the police, as the other man did the wet work of wading through the water of the fountain to collect the coinage.

Now that I am an older man, I know that those men had some mental concerns about themselves. It is not all illegal drugs and alcohol. Those men had lived in homes with

15

Memoirs of a Taxi Driver

families that had no idea that some cataclysmic event was about to happen to those normal looking people. What must be discovered by society is why those people subjugate themselves to those legal and illegal substances.

Sometimes as a boy I would pass those people, dirty, disheveled, and with my mind take them out of their filthy garments and put them in the suits of the business people that follow the sun into the city center, and they would look creditable, they would be those people. And if they looked creditable, I wondered what cataclysmic event happened in their lives to bring them to the station they were presently? Did they have children, grandchildren, what happen to them along the way? When they were born into the world, was there a mother there to take them into her arms and dream dreams for them? When did their cataclysmic downfall begin? I knew some of them were college graduates in my mind, once college professors with class schedules and papers to grade.

It is easy to see those people at night. A taxi driver can see people easier at night standing outside of businesses.

Some of the businesses that were there in the city center when I was a child delivering papers are no longer there.

One morning, while driving through that area, I decided to find a small business that was there, still in existence when I delivered newspapers in the morning as a child. I could find not one small business that I remembered. I did find some larger businesses, but even some of them had either gone out of business or had suffered some kind of bankruptcy.

The older you get, the fewer people and man-made places you see around when you were younger. You start to yearn for the good old days. I think it is a mistake to do that; I try to avoid that practice. Things change. A man cannot stop change in the world. A man has to roll with change around him.

The city center is a different place at night. It is dark and I have time to ponder. That is when I learn. When I ponder, I learn from my past mistakes.

Prologue

I have wondered if people know that pigeons fly around the city center at night? They are the only species of birds that do I think. At night, I might be sitting at a cab stand and see something that looks like a rat walking about, and it is a pigeon walking about the concrete sidewalk pecking at the ground. You have to watch your step if they are sitting somewhere above you. They are known to drop bombs down on people.

I did see a strange thing one night or one matutinal hour while the sun was far away. I was driving north along the lake one morning. I made a left turn onto a street that lay itself through the park and saw a large white bird. It was just sitting there mature in the street, with the city lights reflecting on its big white body. I stopped my taxi and looked at it without moving. I had a camera with me, and I tried to engage the camera before it flew away from the street. But it did fly away before I could take a picture. Because it was three o'clock in the morning, I did not bother to park my car when I saw the bird land nearby at a baseball diamond beyond some trees. It was as beautiful as a woman in a sheer white gown in the evening starlight.

I was tired early in the morning, and I eased my body out of my taxi and languorously tiptoed across the pavement onto the sidewalk to the bushes. Through the bushes and onto the field I went and prepared myself, when, with one giant, silent sweep of its white wings, that snow owl flew away into the darkness. After it had decided to fly away, I did not watch as it disappeared into the darkness. I was so disappointed, and I just stood there in a cloying sort of way, or maybe like one who had been surprised with a cold bucket of water all over one's face suddenly in public.

That is how a woman can decide to leave out of a man's life. One day you are happy and at home with her; the next day she is magically gone from your life.

When it did fly away, it did so without a sound from its wings. Sometimes, even today, when in the park, I will look for one of those snow owls, but I have never seen one since.

17

Memoirs of a Taxi Driver

At night there is peace--especially during the weekdays. People are at home or work. For some reason, on weekends the sanest people on earth become the most insane people on earth. You would never guess that if you saw them on a street walking pass you in the daytime. Talking about these people is the most difficult part of my business. However, almost all the people one might transport in a taxi are good descent people. Are they perfect? No, they are not perfect, but they work everyday and pay their bills. They are credible. Believe this or not about the people I tell you about now, but people you might pick up if you drove a taxi or I might pick up at night are friendlier than those in the daylight hours. It is only you and them at night. The hustle and bustle of the day is over. They know it is just you and them, and there seems to be some bonding that takes place. Everybody needs everybody else in the night. If you go down, you have to depend on that person that might be walking by or driving by to call for help.

But in the daytime, there are so, so many people. If blood is coming out of you, people will walk through your blood to get where they are going because they are busy and have an appointment they have to get to. During the day everybody leaves it up to the other guy to do something to help.

Yes, people are very good at night. People who do not believe that probably read too many newspapers.

Years ago, I stopped at a fast-food restaurant for some sandwiches, and a woman ran in my direction screaming. She was not screaming very loud, but loud enough for me to know that there was a concern about her. She ran up to me with a gun in her hand and said two men had tried to rob her, and with her empty hand she was reaching over her shoulder where she said one of them had shot her in the back and dropped the gun he had used on her. She did not stop for me for long and went to the traffic intersection. Along with me a bus driver and a motorist stopped to help. If that had happened in the daytime with the sun at its

Prologue

zenith, nothing of that sort would have happened. Motorists would have been trying to run over her regardless of her situation.

Once, just before twelve in the morning, I had a flat tire. There was a service station not far down the street but too far to roll or carry a car tire. I just waited for a bus to come by, paid my fare, and rode down to the service station. If that had been during the day, the bus drivers would have said that it would be impossible for him to let me on the bus with that dirty tire. The bus driver that night just let me step right on up with the tire. He let me on because at night there are circumstances that cannot be helped, and exceptions are made. When I sat down in my seat with that tire between my legs, out in the aisle, people started to talk to me about my mishap; we all laughed and made other comments. When I got to the service station, it was not a full-service facility, and the attendant was very busy. He saw my situation, stopped what he was doing and hooked up the air hose which the station kept lock up at all times. Are those people good? Only at night are people that good.

Anytime you pick up a middle-aged man or a middle-aged woman drunk from a bar at two o'clock in the morning, they are immature and need some kind of therapy. These people are not so good to have around. One night I picked up a woman who stood on a corner at an intersection. She had been at a party, not at a bar drinking, but actually at a party with friends. I did not know before I picked her up that she had been drinking, she hid that expertly as she stood at the traffic intersection. However, after she set herself down in the taxi, her drunkenness was apparent.

In her drunkenness behind me, she asked to be taken not far away. As I drove her home, she told me that she was leaving the big city for her small town in Wyoming. I asked her why she would do such a thing when the city had so much to offer anyone who came within its borders. She told me that the men in this city were plastic men and that she could not bear it any longer. All the men she had dated were failures, and the relationships she had with them would not sustain themselves. I asked her if a little bit of the problem could have been herself, and she told me that she was not the problem in the relationships she had with those men she spoke of. I asked her indirectly if she had hoped to marry any of those men, and her answer was affirmative.

Before I discharged her, I did ask her if she thought that any decent man would want to marry a woman that was a drunkard such as herself, and there was a long pause before she began to rationalize. I cannot remember where I dropped that woman off, but I did drop her off never to see her again in the city.

I am older now; I am a little wiser now. I understand that woman had a concern that only a psychologist or psychiatrist could service. Something happened in her life that caused her to be in that way. If she did get married, her husband would have to be very patient with her to fulfill the marriage vows. Not enough men understand the foibles of women.

Life is not a bowl of cherries with women. Not only is it not a bowl of cherries with women, it is not a bowl of cherries with men. There is always a man out there out of his mind. One night while driving in the city center, which I explained earlier to be my favorite venue to drive in, I came upon a man at a corner with his trousers and underwear pulled down to his ankles, dancing around in a circle holding his head back into the air with his eyes closed. I had my camera in the trunk of my taxi and stopped my taxi to retrieve it. When I opened the trunk, the camera was not there. That photograph would have been one of the best I had ever taken. It was so late, there were no people or vehicular traffic; I had plenty of time to focus and shoot. I sometimes think about how foolish I was not to have my camera that time. I had to drive on without having taken that photograph.

I have pictures of police officers sleeping in squad cars. I discover more police officers sleeping in squad cars than I

Prologue

do taxi drivers. It is not proper what they do, but it is done more than a woman can blink her eye in a day. I once was driving down a street on the far north side of town. As I passed a small shopping plaza, I sighted two uniformed police officers asleep in a squad car. I continued on my way and was lucky enough to roll up next to a police sergeant in a squad car not a block away. I stopped and mentioned to him that two uniformed officers were asleep in a squad car up the street. He told me that he hoped they would be, because they were working, guarding a store that had been burglarized.

Once I caught a police officer having sex with a prostitute. I was parked in the city park near the lake on a street between cars. It was impossible to see me, because I was lying down on my right side in the front seat taking a short nap before I resumed my driving. I had been sleeping for about an hour and was refreshed enough to restart my shift again. I rose up in front of the steering wheel. I saw a police sergeant parked about ten feet in front of me. On the right rear side of his squad car he had a prostitute standing outside the squad car, bent over, with her upper torso inside the squad car with her panties down around her thighs. The sergeant was humping her from behind—I'll tell you more about that in a story I want to share with you

I sat there amazed at first and smiling in the end without them knowing I was there. I did not move, but when he finished his work, he saw me, repaired himself, said a few words to the woman, had her sit down in the squad car, walked around to his door, and drove away embarrassed I surmised. I knew the prostitute—I'll tell you about that late. I tell that story every time I can remember to tell it.

Do not let your mind play games with you and have you think you can trust a police officer. You cannot really trust a police officer if you are poor, uneducated, or a minority. I say this because if you look at the statistics, these are the people that are killed by them, arrested by them, and sent to prison on false police reports. When you see the police coming, you must see criminals coming. Should we expect better from our city police in a large city? I cannot tell you that. They come from the very neighborhood I grew up in. They are human. They have hate and love in their hearts as I do. Everyday I drive I notice that I do some kind of traffic infraction. When you see the police coming in the city, see a law-breaker coming. See yourself coming, and watch your rear. I warn you now.

Understand, the police see traffic infractions all the time and do not stop people. They usually do not want to be bothered with people. Stopping people can be dangerous. They have families; they want to get home at night. Especially if it is near a shift change and those police officers are trying to get home.

There was a bar that I once sat outside of on the weekends. There was a stop sign there. I watched to see if the drivers of cars would make a complete stop at that stop sign. Would you believe that I sat there collectively for four hours, not one vehicle would make a complete stop for the stop sign, including the city police?

People on the weekends drive intoxicated all the time. The police do not want to be bothered with those people. I once picked up a passenger who had been driving intoxicated at a stoplight. He told me a police officer walked over to his car at the stoplight, saw that he was intoxicated, told him to park his car, and let the man walk home. She could have put him under the jail, but it was a busy weekend, and she was directing heavy traffic.

The police have to deal with prostitutes. There are prostitutes all over the city. Prostitutes do not solicit children. I say that to you now because as a child a prostitute never solicited me. They are in most cases out for financial returns for services provided, and children do not have enough money for their services in most cases. When I first started driving at night, I would see women sitting on benches at the bus stops waiting for the buses. But two hours later, driving by the same bus stop, I would see the same woman sitting at the bench, at the same bus stop, waiting for a bus. Sometimes the bus drivers would pass her up without any protest whatsoever from her. Then, the truth finally came to me.

One night on a block that the prostitutes work, one female in the apparel of a prostitute haled me. I attempted to pass her without an iota from me that I had noticed her, but she haled me as though she required my services. I did slow to lower my window, and she asked me if I would drive her to a suburb far from the city. Her costume was scintillating, and as the cars went by, the headlights would simmer across it. I looked at her and asked her if she had the money in her pocket and on her person. She told me that she had that money with her in her pocket. I granted her request, and she set herself down behind me and gave me my directions, and I started my taxi in the direction she had requested.

She told me business had been slow that night and asked if there was a convention in town. I told her that I did not know about a convention being in town, but business was almost always good for me. She had a large bag with her. As I drove she opened it. I heard things moving about within that bag she carried, and she began to move her body around in a way that is not common for a passenger in a taxi. When the sounds became too bizarre and her body movements became too unorthodox, I turned to look around and saw her removing her working costume to replace it with that of a suburban housewife. But what was more unusual than any of that was that she was pregnant many months already.

I asked her if she was pregnant, and she told me that she was pregnant. I inquired why she worked while pregnant, and she would not tell me. She did tell me if her potential customers knew she was pregnant, they would not hire her. We drove on until we came to her destination, which was a beautiful house on a beautiful block. She paid me, and I watched her as she walked away from the taxi into its confines.

Memoirs of a Taxi Driver

What is best about the taxi business besides the financial rewards, are the stories. The stories you always learn from; you never forget. I have stories to tell; I have wisdom to share.

With a Strong Ear

"I was born in a desert place. When the wind blew, the food and other important products had to be covered, or they would be full of the sand that went about in the wind. It was almost always hot there, and the rain did not always fall there. To survive my people hunted the animals in the area, and they gathered the foods that grew below and above the earth. They knew all the secret places to find water when it was scarce. When the water was not enough, we were always moving about to find it. There could not be a miscalculation in finding that water. It was a matter of life and death in my land. When the water was sufficient, after the rains had come, we feasted in plenty, and we did not move about as much. Our villages grew from a few people to many people. There was dancing and other social activities when the rains had come.

"Both of my parents where born in that place as their parents were born in that place, as those before them. My mother was a good woman. She knew where all the mongongo nuts grew, and with her digging stick she dug the roots of the klaru to make sure food was there on my father's return. She did not accept my father immediately. She, in fact, detested him. Her marriage was arranged before she was twelve, as all marriages have been amongst my people before there were recorded words. She did everything possible to ruin the marriage. My father could not have tried to be a better husband. He was patient, kind, and understanding to my mother. But it was years before she finally accepted him.

"As a youth I would run and play with the other children, as children will. There was no other interest in my mind and heart but play. I would do this day in and day out until the sun stood red in the west sky. When I closed my eyes in the nighttime darkness, it was like magic, and the sun would be up in my eyes with its yellow flames when the morning came. When I grew older, my father took me to hunt the springhare, and, when I grew even older and more of a young man, he taught me the ways of the antelope and showed me how to capture it in a trap. It was good to be alive then. There were no times more exciting, more wonderful.

"It is only when I saw Chako, in a village that my father and I had stopped in for the evening that my heart became a thunder inside of me. She was so beautiful, so exceedingly enchanting, I could not remove my eyes from her. She was tall but tiny in structure, and when she stood to converse with another, she stood with her legs slightly apart with both arms at her sides. Never in my life had I seen a girl more graceful in motion. I saw her and knew that I wanted her for myself. I told my father on our way back to our village the next day about that girl. He told me that I was still too young and that, when I learned to hunt as a man, the time would be right for a wife.

"I told my mother about the beautiful girl I had seen and how I wanted her, and she laughed the sound of a mother. But I knew what I wanted, and it was Chako, and I would have her even though I was thought to be too young with no hair about my face.

"I followed my father out to hunt without his comments. I watched my father and walked the walk he walked and mimicked his hands and other jesters. With that, and from there, I tried to be a man and to leave childish thoughts and play behind me. I became one of the best hunters in the village with my father's knowledge in me. Even the elders would come for me on treks through the bush that surrounded us to guarantee a successful hunt. It was natural for me to hunt. I had some sort of sixth sense and could almost smell the springhare outside of its burrow. I was quick on my feet, strong and untiring. My arrow was straight and true; my arrow never failed.

"However, I never forgot about that fair girl. One day early before the sun rose, I started out for her village without my parents' consent. On the second day, on my arrival, with the sun high, I came to her place. I went to the hut of Chako with a springhare I had caught along the way. I introduced myself to her parents and told them that my eyes had seen Chako and that one day I would marry her. As I spoke those words, I looked at Chako, and with eyes of a cat she looked at me and smiled with astonishment, turning her face from mine. She could not remember me, for her eyes did not see me with the interest of a woman on that day I had visited her village with my father but only as a young girl with interest in play.

"Her parents told me Chako had been given to someone else and that I was not yet a man. I could not provide for her as a man, and I did not yet know the way of the land and the antelope to have a wife. She had been pledged. They laughed at me softly. Some hours later my father, after following my tracks, came into the village to find me. He scolded me for leaving our village. He said it was too dangerous for a child of my age to do so. A hyena or some other wild animal could have killed me and eaten me.

"I was so young and yet so concerned about this girl that I mentioned her to my father and mother everyday. They laughed quite often, but in time, they became more serious in their denial of my youthful passion for that girl, for I returned to her village time and again over the months and years, and the branches my father used on me did not keep me in our hut.

"I hunted the antelope and caught the springhare and laid them at the hut of her parents. They were cold to me at first, but with my persistence they warmed to me and made a place for me at their fire. They were kind to me because of my efforts, but they were steadfast that Chako would marry another from a village a day and a half away. I was too young for her they told me. Chako needed a man who was older and wiser to the ways of the land and its beginnings. I would soon lose interest in Chako, as young men do, they would tell me. Their daughter had to have a husband that was older, more stable.

"That rejection did not diminish the thunder in my heart, and I went forth into the bush to bring back what your people called an eland. I followed it into the bush with the sand hot under my feet and let the arrow with its poison do its work. It is the biggest of all antelope of our place, and I stood over it with my chest swollen with the pride of a man. With the help of my family, who had eventually given their hearts to my love for Chako, we carried the flesh of the animal to the hut of Chako's parents. I stood before Chako's father and told him I had no time to sit and eat the flesh of the animal I had brought to him, but my father and mother would sit with him to eat the flesh. My job as a man was to know the land that I would support my family with; I would hunt and work as a man in the desert sand.

"I went forward into the morning sunrise the next day as I had seen my father do as a child and slept in the bush that surrounded me for not less than two days to bring a second eland to the ground and to the hut of the one I loved. On my return even my father was with large eyes and loss of words. I stood before them and laid the animal to the ground. In that way is how Chako became mine, and my father and her father made the arrangements and began the construction of the hut that I would live in with my new wife.

With a Strong Ear

"On the day of our marriage many friends and relatives came from the near places and far places that surrounded us. The people danced and chanted all the day and late into the night. That evening my wife was carried and placed down inside our hut, and I sat in front of that hut, which is the custom of my people. Before the sun went away completely from the sky, a caravan of machines that carried the Hereros came to our village. Their machines carried many men. Those men were rich in the knowledge of the outside world. Their eyes understood the books with the magic words. And when they spoke, they spoke in the language I speak to you in now. My people are a more simple people, we do not know those magic words; we live from the land that surrounds us and hunt the animals that walk it.

"They came with smiles on their faces, and they watched with satisfaction the ceremony. When my bride came from the hut to observe the men and their machines, I saw the eyes of the Herero men look upon the love that I would die to possess, that girl that I would run down the springhare and the swift antelope of the bush of my land to make mine. She was more beautiful than all the women of my village, than all the women in all the villages in my land the sun brought light to in its daily visits. The beauty of the beads around her throat was invisible with her skin so good, so perfect. She was mine; she was my wife; and I would work for her until my life went from my body.

"When she appeared they looked swiftly at her with eyes that were untrue. There was one Herero man who was taller than the others, with the clothing of the outside places. With skin so black, so dark, so rich, he was one with the darkness and stood like a giant away from the fires. He seemed to be the headman amongst them, and he gave them directions on his arrival. He studied my bride with eyes that wanted her as my eyes had wanted her. His smile was a smile that I had felt upon my face but could never see when my eyes first came on Chako.

Memoirs of a Taxi Driver

"That tall one saw the concern in my face. He went back to his machines and approached my people and I, who all wished me happiness, with gifts and treasures. He handed them out to everyone, and he took out black bottles that contained liquid that burn the throat and made the people happy.

"He came to me and held the bottle to his mouth and placed it in my hand and signaled to me to drink from it. It was hot in my mouth, but, after it had gone down into my body, it became warm and made me feel happy as a child. He placed his arm about me and signaled for me to drink the liquid again, and I did drink. Again, again, and again I tasted the hot liquid that became warm inside of me, and I became happy like a child and began to dance about. The people and the huts began to go around me without stopping, and I could not stop their movement. I fell to the ground, and the ground would move without me moving. I fell to my back, and the stars moved in a circle around my eyes, and I then heard the voice of my wife scream as if a desert lion had come from out of the sand to attack her.

"I looked to the sound of her voice and saw the Tall Herero with his arms around her as he pulled her to the machines that rolled across the sand. She fought at him, digging her hands into his face. I tried to stand, but I could not stand because my legs would not be strong under me, and I fell to the sand on my hands and onto my face many times as I tried to reach her. My people chased after them as they went across the sand in those machines, but they too, had the liquid in them that burned and made them happy as a child, and they could not hold the Hereros. The Hereors were strong and fast; they beat my people off with weapons.

"They went off into the night, and the machines that carried them made less noise as they went farther from my village. I ran after them, but, as I said, my legs were not strong under me, and my body was not quick enough for those machines. I ran as a wounded antelope with the poison arrow in its body before it falls to follow the machines that carried my love, my wife, whom no woman in my village or all the villages in my land were as beautiful.

"It was dark, and I could not see the feet of those machines that went across the sand, and my body would not do its work for me. I fell down many times, but I continued until the sun began to rise behind me.

"I walked and ran all that day and did not stop to hunt but only ate the roots and drank the water I knew was nearby. That night I did not sleep but walked through the night, and, when the sun came to the sky in the morning, I continued to follow the machines until my head began to hurt inside from no rest. I continued all that day, walking farther from my land until I was in a place that my people did not know and I had never seen. The land began to change around me, and there were no bushes as in my land, but only sand; I went into that land and followed the feet of the machines. On the next morning, I came upon a campsite that the Hereros had made in the sand. I found a necklace of beads my love, my wife, whom I would love until the life left my body, had worn on our wedding night. Tears came from my eyes, and I continued on without stopping all through the sun-heat of the day. On I went until it seemed to be another place. There was sand all around, and, to find the water I needed, I had to dig into the earth many feet down.

"When it became too hot for me to go through the desert, I slept in the day and traveled in the night darkness. I was so lost in my heart, that the wild animals about me I had no fear of, and they seemed to know I would have killed them, because, I now feel, and see, how wild I was in my pursuit of the Hereros. I was insane with grief. For days and weeks I went on, and, when the desert winds came to wipe away the tracks of their machines, it took sometimes days to find them again. On I went across the sand until one day I saw birds in the sky with their white wings above me. On I went until the smell of the land became different; on and on I went to follow the tracks until I came to a large liquid body with a giant motion I had never seen, or knew existed. I looked down unto its vastness so great. Never had I seen a body of water so large. I looked only a moment upon it; I was insane inside myself with loss, and I went on.

"Across the sand of the beach I ran to follow the tracks. On I went until I came across the carcass of a dead sea-beast and a desert lion feeding upon it. Unafraid, and with a spear I had made alone the way, I made loud noises and made myself as large as possible to frighten away the lion beast. I only ate a moment and ran on to follow the tracks of the machines.

"I went on for another day, and on that day, I saw footprints of the Hereros. I studied them for some time and heard voices from behind a sand mountain that reached out into the great water. I climbed it and saw the camp of the Hereros. In that camp there were many more of them than the night in my village. The camp had been there for many days, and there where men in large floating branches that came to and went away from the land to a larger floating branch, larger than all the floating branches on all the bushes and trees in my land. I had never seen such a large floating branch. On those branches men stood and walked around, and they loaded items on the smaller branches that came to shore in the great liquid.

"I looked for Chako and could not see her amongst the people who went about the camp. I came closer to the camp, and I saw the Tall Herero that had taken my wife from me standing, giving directions as a headman to the others. My eyes followed him because I knew my love would be near him. Like a bird with arrow-eyes, I did not let my eyes go from him. He directed his men and bent his tall black body down to show them where to reach for things in the tents that sheltered them from the sand and sun. He placed things onto the boxes they carried as they loaded the smaller water branches and moved away.

"As they loaded those branches something fell to the ground, and the Tall Hereor bent to pick up Chako's kaross.

With a Strong Ear

He placed it onto the boxes that his men carried and pointed out to the floating branch that was larger than all the branches and all the trees in my land. He stood there directing the men who worked at his words and boarded the last of the floating branches, waving to the Hereors who remained on the shore. I made my body one with the sand and came closer to that camp to place myself into one of those floating branches, but I could not find one to cross the water. I lay hidden in the sand as the Hereors loaded and broke away the camp and placed its remnants into their desert machines. I waited and waited until they departed, and I took myself into their camp and walked the water's edge to stare at the floating branch larger than all branches.

"I could not swim, and there were no branches left for me to cross the water. I stepped out into the water to float my body across to the floating branch, but I sank to the bottom of the water drinking very much of it, but pulling myself to shore before I died.

"There were many boxes made of wood and string around the camp, and I went about tying the wood and boxes together to make a floating branch large enough to carry me. Before I could finish my floating branch, the giant floating branch off the shore began to move away from me. I hurried and finished the best I could, and I began to make my way towards its vastness on my stomach, making my arms work for me.

"On I went in the direction of the branch as it moved away from me. I went on until I could not see it with my eyes and only moved my arms in the direction of it. I went on into the late afternoon until my arms became no good to me, and I just lay on the branches to sleep. When my eyes opened, it was darkness all around me, and I did not know were the shore was for me. The water became bigger than I had ever seen water, and it broke around me. I held on through the night, and I did not let go. When the sun came back to the earth, the water became kind again, and I used my arms to go in the direction of the branch that took my wife, my love, the one I would love until my life went from my body.

"I went on until my water was all gone and the dried roots and caterpillars were all eaten. After three sunrises I had no arms to move me about, and at night and during the day large sea animals with arrowheads growing from their backs came from out of the water to brush up against me. My feet would hang from my floating branches, and I would have to hold them above the water to keep them away from those animals. When my legs became tired, I would push them away with my feet.

"I floated along for days, and the sea animals would follow me without rest. There was no water for me to drink, my mind did not work, my eyes did not see, and I would leave the world and sleep and wake repeatedly. I saw Chako's face many times in front of me. She smiled at me to wake me in the morning before I left for the hunt with her father. She shook me with her one hand, and I smiled, and then she shook me with both hands. When I did not wake, she shook me again, and in my face, I felt water and a strange man's face came to replaced that of Chako's in front of mine, calling out to me to drink the water, and I did taste water, and my lips reached out to possess it.

"After I had drunk from that water given by that strange face, I realized I was in a strange place that rocked like the water that had carried me on my bundle of branches. I could not see the waves but only heard them. The man tried to talk to me, but I did not know his words. When my life came back to me, I spoke to the strange face and other faces on that ship, and they did not speak my words or know their meaning.

"I rested some days, and they took me along with them to a northern place were there was snow; they worked with instruments to measure the ice and snow. I had never known a place with such cold, such ice, and my bones would rock even though I had many garments upon my body. I worked in their kitchen to wash the dishes, and, when I learned

With a Strong Ear

some of their words, they would take me along to hold some of their instruments, but my English never became good enough for me to tell them the true pain that was in my heart. However, they realized I was looking for a woman that was very important to me.

"We continued on into the north and anchored on islands that were many in that place with the snow and ice. Dogs were brought from the stomach of the vessel and hitched to wooden branches that were pulled across the ice. Many times we almost went below the ice through the holes that would appear without warning. We were weeks upon that ice, and we visited many villages where there were no antelope or springhare, and the people and children seemed not to notice the cold and danced about without many garments upon their bodies in the snow. They only ate fish and sea animals, and from those sea animals they used the skins to make garments to protect themselves from the wind when it came.

"After some months they went back to their land and left me with their headmen. Their headmen put me in a place that had food and other comforts that people of my circumstance would need. One of their headmen told me that the raft that I had made with the boxes came from a ship that was destined for a place called New York City. I did not know that place New York City. They asked me if I would like to go back to the place of my people, and I told them of my wife and the Tall Hereor and Hereros that had taken her away from me. I told them I wanted to go to that place called New York to find my wife I loved so much.

"They could not understand my ache for her. They did not know the heat of the sun and the hunts to impress her and her parents of my worthiness. They did not know how I wanted to become old with her. They said that it was impossible for me to go to New York City and that I would have to go back to my home if the main headman found it to be so.

Memoirs of a Taxi Driver

"I ran from that place and walked the streets of their city, asking people for that place of New York City. I had some of their paper with the headlady upon it and used it to ride to London. In London I made money by sweeping in front of businesses. I ate their food with that money, and I slept under a bridge in the night. I saved my money and paid a kind woman to let me sleep in her garage, but she refused to let me sleep there and insisted that I sleep in her servants' quarters. I worked for her, and in that way I made more money and went to a school to study their language.

"After working for her for sometime, I saved even more money and decided to leave for New York City to find my wife. I had no papers or knowledge to leave that country, but found a ship that was sailing to that place called New York City and stowed away there for the trip. I hide myself thoroughly, and when the ship arrived in New York City, I heard the people knocking around for a person that might be hidden away such as myself. When the nighttime came, I slipped away from that place and tried to find Chako, but that New York City was too large for me. I did not and could not find my way. I slept underground with people of my kind, and found a job delivering newspapers in the morning before the sun came. I read those papers, reading them for a word or picture of Chako.

"One day an idea came inside of me. I went to the shipping yard and asked about the ship that I was told my raft was made of. I asked around at the yards where that ship floated, and no one knew of the ship. I did not give up, and I kept visiting that place. Finally, I was told about a small ship that came into port only when the leaves fell in the autumn, one owned by a mining company that was in a desert place called Nevada.

"I did not know that place Nevada, but with a map, I found Nevada, and rode the buses to that place called Reno in Nevada. I went to stand outside the building where that company did its business, to watch for the Tall Hereor or my Chako. I lived in front of that place almost twelve hours

With a Strong Ear

a day, watching the people that came and went inside. One day, I stood in front of that building that was tall to the sky, reading the newspaper so as not to look too obvious when I saw the picture of the Tall Heroro in the newspaper. He had been promoted in his company and was the headman of their European offices. My heart came to my throat, and I headed to that place in Europe. With maps from the libraries to study, I found my way to Europe through wicked deeds for those who wished for a body to carry illegal things, and in Germany I came from the plane after fulfilling my work and left for my journey to find my Chako, the one I loved and needed so passionately.

"I went to the place of that Tall Hereor's business but could not find him entering or leaving. I did not know the language, and with the money I had earned and saved, I rented a hotel room and paid a school to teach me the words of those people. At night I would study in a school, and in the day I would watch outside of that place of business the Tall Hereor was important. But the Tall Hereor never came to that place to work.

"I could speak some words of that land but not enough to be clear in understanding with those people. I decided to hire a private detective to find the place of that Herero, and when he gave me the Tall Herero's place to sleep and eat, I went to that place of the Tall Hereor. On the front door I knocked, and a woman servant came to the door as they do in their dress and told me he was out of the country with his wife and would not be back until a month had past. My heart became heavy, and to avoid suspicion I turned away from that place and walked away, leaving my name and number behind. In the day, and into the night, I secretly watched the house until I knew the day and time that female servant would not be there. And on a night that I knew she would be absent I came close to the house. In the darkness I became invisible. On the ground and through the shrubbery my hand came to the basement door, and with quiet strength I forced the door open.

37

Memoirs of a Taxi Driver

"I went about the house until I came to the bedroom of the Tall Herero, and with the eyes of a night bird, I saw the possessions of that man. On the night table I saw pictures of him with his arms around Chako and the smile on her face that she smiled when she had been with me. On the dresser there was the cologne and perfume she wore. In the drawers there were the garments she wore under the clothing she wore in the closets. I touched many things that they had together and walked about the house unmolested to see where he had brought my Chako. Before my time was up, I went from their home back into the night.

"With a phone call and cleverness, I asked his secretary where I could write to the Tall Herero in the States, and she gave me the address, and I was on a plane to that place in California. On my arrival, he and his wife were in Mexico to study the land that his business was a part of. I went to the south across the border to where his company was to be. In that place, I was told that he was to be in Peru, and I left through the isthmus to the city called Lima. In that city I arrived just as they had left, but my money was not enough to follow them. Being in that way, I found the people who worked during the night to carry the things illegally across the borders to the United States. I took the job to do that work, and I started across the land of Peru to the Gulf to meet my boat.

"Along the way, and because of that, is how the police stopped me, and they found the illegal things that I carried in my truck. They took me to the cell and forced me to tell my purpose. I explained to them that I was from a desert country where the springhare ran fast across the sand and the antelope leaped higher than any antelope on the earth. They insisted that I reveal my sources and true purpose, and they beat me about the head with a large book that pages came out of on delivery to my head.

"I tried to explain to them that I had come for my wife, that she had been taken from me by the Hereors to that side of the earth. They continued to beat me until I lost my senses and awoke in a place that had many flies and other insects within its confines. There, I was kept for one year and then taken along with my companions to a larger place that was worse than the first.

"In that country I knew no family, and I had to eat the food the other prisoners did not eat that their families brought them. I was sick many months, and as the months turned into years, I grew sores about me and did not look like the child my father taught the ways of the bush. My face was a thing of horror to look at, my body was swollen with puss all about it, and my comrades demanded that I be taken from them or treated with the medicine that the hospital would have.

"Because of that, I was placed in the hospital at the end of my life with little security, and in that way I made my escape through the daytime window to hide in the countryside. I became one with the land, and the dogs made their sounds in pursuit of me as I made my way to the east to the rain forest. After many weeks of travel over the land and through the rivers, I came to the heart of the rain forest to a place that was not near the Gulf. I had seen the tracks of the many Indian peoples in the forest, but I avoided them, for I knew not what their reaction would be to a strange man about. I stood one morning at a distance to observe a forest village, trying to make my way around it, when, from my rear, came an arrow that went through my calf into a tree to hold me close to it. As I tried to free my body from that tree, many of the Indian people came from out of their hiding places to beat me with weapons that made me unconscious.

"When I came back to life, I was lying in their village center with the people around me, and the men and children threatening to strike me if my movements were too rapid. I did not speak their words, and upon trying to raise myself I fell back once again into unconsciousness. When I awoke a second time, I was in a covered shelter with my leg bandaged, and some men with their native paint about their faces and bodies. One of them offered me water to drink and food. The food was good to me, the water was needed, and afterwards I became more alert to the surroundings about me. I tried to converse with the people, but there was no understanding. When I moved too rapidly, the men raised their weapons. In the distance I saw the children playing with their bows and arrows aimed at a slow moving turtle. I beckoned to the men to give me a bow with an arrow. When it was handed to me with some caution, I raised myself to find a target that I could impress my nervous hosts with.

"Through the village a small sparrow made its way through the huts that made its center. Quicker than a hummingbird, I raised the bow and arrow and cut the bird surgically in half. I stayed with those people until two rainy seasons had passed, and I finally made my way to the north where the Gulf meets the land. There, next to the jungle, the salty water came to meet the shore, and I had no way to make it across that water. I walked until I came to some villages. I was not dressed properly with only a loincloth to cover me. I searched the dumpsters for clothing that was more presentable, and I came from the forest to mingle with the village people about.

"There was no work for a person in such a small village, and I walked along the shore to make my way finally to Bogotá to find work. I went to where the ships came into the ports to find work. I had no papers; I had no home, so I did the work above that of an animal and saved my money until I had enough to place in a bank in the city. I bought clothing for myself. I sold handkerchiefs on the city streets, and I eventually rented a small cottage just outside the city limits. In the daytime sky I sold the handkerchief with the help of the Yanomamo from the forest to the south. I had many workers, and I became wealthy enough to hire a boat to place me on the shores near Miami in the night.

"I flew to California to the place of the Tall Herero. No building stood where a building had stood before. I flew to Reno, and in that place stood another business. I became

With a Strong Ear

lost in my thoughts and looked in the telephone books for this company that the Tall Herero was important in. I could not find that place. I went to the library of the city and searched the past newspapers to find the cause of its disappearance. In that way, I found the company existed no more because of money problems, and it had melted away without the currency it needed to survive.

"When I found the Hereor, he lived with Chako outside the city of Reno in a small town that was not the place of the rich as he had been. His money was gone, and the desert machine he drove was full of sand and rust. He worked in the desert to find the gold dust that would bring him back to life in the world.

"I went into the desert away from them and stood off in the distance to study his plans. After some long time, I left for the most far places of the desert, and it is there that I found the place I would bring him to with my wife, the love I would love until my life was no more in me. After my plan was complete, I went to his home in a business manner. Chako sat by his side as I explained to him that I had known about him and his company for many years. Chako did not know me, for the time had changed me, and she had lived a life that was high, and I did not matter.

"I told him I had searched for him because of his knowledge and business prowess, and the gold I knew to be in the desert was there. Because of his knowledge and expertise, I told him I would pay him to travel with me, and, if the veins were true, I would split the wealth with him and his wife.

"His voice was excited, as he held the hand of my love with his giant hand, and brought it to his mouth to kiss it. He proclaimed that hope had come to them finally. Inside of me a fire burned, and I wanted to leap into his heart with a knife to stop it, but I thought of all I had been through, the short time that remained, and the fire in me became quiet as the beads of sweat cooled my head. It would be only a few days until my plan was complete.

Memoirs of a Taxi Driver

"We made ready with a new jeep machine I had bought with supplies and water for the journey. In the desert we left the main road and drove into the sand. We went far, and in the night, when he slept with Chako in the tent across from me, my hands trembled with rage and contempt, but I became calm, and my rage rolled over in me with a quiet thunder.

"When we could go no farther, we left the jeep machine and walked the rest of the way up the mountains to the place I said the gold vein would be. After a short time, I told them that I had not brought enough water and had to go back to the jeep to retrieve more. They waited for me, and at the jeep I made a small hole in the gas tank, let the water run out of the containers into the sand, and went back to them to continue into the desert mountains to the false gold. We traveled into the late morning and hid ourselves from the sun in the noontime heat. When the sun left the sky enough for us to travel, we went on through the mountains.

"I appeared to make myself not know the way in their eyes and hesitated many times in my remembrance. In that way, I prolonged the trip for more days until our water had run low in its supply. When the water was gone from our possession, I encouraged them to go on because water was near us. We all became dry with thirst, and I asked them to wait, for I deceived them into thinking I was going a distance to find my directions. In that way I would go to the water that I had stored in the desert in a secret place ahead of our arrival.

"On my return I deceived thirst, breathed like one who would be thirsty and wiped my brow with false weakness and exhaustion. When I saw the Tall Herero was dry without water, and we were days from the jeep, I pleaded that it was hopeless and that we should return to the jeep and take our chances on finding water on the way. They all agreed. We walked into the sun and rested in the noontime. When the last of the water was amongst us, the Tall Hereor took Chako's hand in his and insisted that she drink the last.

42

With a Strong Ear

She would not, and he returned it to her hand and kissed her good skin so beautiful about her cheek. He spoke softly into her ear, and she held the vessel to her mouth to drink. He was strong inside his heart; he was brave.

"After she had drunk the last of the water, he took his giant hand and stroke it down her hair and placed his cheek upon it, speaking soft words unheard to my ear. She looked up at him not completely and compassionately touched her head against his chest.

"We continued on through the mountain heat, and because of our weakened states—when the Tall Herero continued in the correct direction—I would insist that it was the wrong direction to deceive him. With words of persuasion from me, the Tall Herero would not question, and we continued on in the wrong direction to prolong our circumstance. When we came to a most dangerous part of our return, I insisted that crossing a narrow path along the side of a shelved abyss would shorten our return by hours. Upon reaching that narrow trail that made its path along the side of that deep shelved abyss, I insisted that the Tall Hereor go to the other side before Chako to anchor the rope so that she could cross along its side safely as we both secured her with the rope.

"On his way down the path along the side of the abyss, he fell many feet into it. It took all my strength to hold Chako from following with hers screams after him. I pointed to a distant point that would take us down to him, and I, and she, went down to where he lay. His knee would not move him, and Chako went all over him with tears from her eyes. She made him comfortable, and I, with my false concern, did what I could.

"She stood up from the ground with her weak legs and looked around the deep abyss to assess an escape. She realized that without water we would perish in the rocks and sand. She stood with her legs slightly apart with her hands hanging at her sides as she had as a child, removed the shovel from her pack and began to dig in the sand for water.

I helped her with an effort that would satisfy any person that would have seen me, but in the end, there was not water, and we all lay down to die in that desert.

"When they were without strength, I crawled away from them and drank the water that I had stored and went back to my place to play my part. When they were both without their senses, I whispered to Chako that I had found water and needed her help to carry it back to them.

"She was without her senses, and I picked her up in my arms and carried her a great distance away from the Tall Hereor to the water I had stored. With some water she became revived and was herself, but weak in her legs. I told her to wait, for I would return to the Tall Hereor to bring him the water.

"I walked through the desert to the abyss where he lay to place enough water in his mouth to bring him hungry to his senses. It is in that way, when he could see me, and understand me, that I placed my mouth close to his ear and told him the night of my marriage and the machines he had come in to steal my wife I loved more than my life and the one I would die for.

"With my mouth to his ear, his eyes became big like that of the owl, and he turned his whole face to mine, his nose touching mine, and looked into my face. With that knowledge he tried to raise himself and swing his arm at me, but he fell back onto the mountain rocks. I sat beside him for many hours and looked into his face as his breaths became slow. My heart became soft for him; but when I thought about the past it became ice in my chest.

"When the end came, I lay down next to him with my nose touching his nose and watched until he moved no desert sand with his breaths. And after awhile, I placed the water to his mouth and it did not go down into him.

"I went back to Chako and met her half way as she was following my tracks back to the abyss. When I met her, I told her the Tall Herero moved no more on my arrival and that my efforts to bring the life back into him had no

With a Strong Ear

powers. Raising her head back into the desert night, she screamed as a mad woman would. Without tiring, she staggered pass me to the place where his body lay. When we reached his place, she lay across his body for many hours making the sounds of a child lost. When she could cry no more, I went to her to lift her up to sit next to me.

"I spoke to her in our language, and her eyes also grew large like that of the owl. Tears came to my eyes, and I began to tell the story of the night of our marriage, the love I had for her that carried me across the earth to find her, and all the pain I had endured. I told her everything as I tell you now.

"She listened with a strong ear without questions to me. She allowed me to come close to her, to touch her arm with my story. With a soft voice and a soft hand that I had wanted, she placed my head against her breast to comfort my sorrow, which I had hoped she would do, and with a secret speed she dashed my eye out of my head with a large stone onto the ground. I could not stop her, and she dashed me in the face many times to break my nose and to cut my lips deep to the white flesh.

"With my eye gone from my head and little water, I walked the distance to the jeep falling many times with the sand in my wounds. I could not find all the secret places I had placed my supply of water, and I lost my senses and only through luck did I come to this cabin."

The woman's hand shook nervously as she placed another bandage across his mouth to absorb blood that had oozed out of the stitches in his lips.

"Abrom, do not let him talk any more; his lip is bleeding."

"One moment, Honey."

"The girl, Chako, what happened to her?"

"They are there now in the sand. My heart was not in me after she dashed me many times with the sharp stone. I tried to give her water, but she would not take it from me. She only moved away from me, pulling the Tall Herero with her until her last strength left her. When she could not move any more without her strength, I poured water into her lips--but she only spit it out with her last power."

"Governor, let's postpone this hunting trip; let me take him to the station."

"No, Sam, this is something the law can not deal with."

"I'm the Superintendent of Police. He's got to be charged."

"Don't forget who got you the job, Mr. Superintendent."

A soft desert breeze came from the open window, blowing small grains of sand onto the wooden floor, whirling it about unnoticed in the cabin quiet.

Hospice for a Snow Bird

I remembered hearing a "thump" in my office that night while sleeping, and I went to investigate the next morning before leaving for class. At first, the size of the creature startled me as it lay near my gable over my garage. Every fall I would find a sparrow or starling in our yard stunned from the impact, a victim of night navigation, but that was a large bird, a goose of Canada. I looked at it for a long time and observed its breast inhaling the autumn air that caused its great heart to beat. Its journey was a long and distant flight over forests, rivers, mountains, and valleys to its winter refuge to the south.

Its head lay to its left side, large and huge, each feather undisturbed in its turmoil. I tapped sheepishly at the window to stir a response. It did raise its head to peer at me with a slanted eye and then regressed to its previous state. I wondered from where it had flown, and I desperately wanted to stroke its breast. Raising the window ever so carefully—it seemed to take forever—snatching my hand away many times for fear, I finally touched the feathers that grew from its breast and felt its warmth come to my fingertips.

Memoirs of a Taxi Driver

With my hand I became more courageous, stroking the great folded wings with no alarm forthcoming from it as it lay nigh my inquisitive fingertips. I explored the back of the giant head, stroking it as a mother would an ill child, stroking the great head I had seen at a distance many times before, as its brethren made their way down to New York State, but which I had never touched.

On my return home that evening, I peeked through the window at a distance and saw that goose unmoved as raindrops began to fall upon it. I sat a prolonged period, watching it from across the room, wondering of its pain, watching its breath expand its breast, the feathers covering it unmolested by the rain. I worked as a mouse in my office that night, surgically performing my chores, picking quietly here and tiptoeing quietly there until bedtime.

I remembered my father telling my sister and I as children, when a sparrow lie before us in the shrubbery to "never touch it, never disturb it, for it is only stunned and will recover after resting." He would always speak those words in a whisper, as though it was a secret for us only to know, whenever a bird rammed our house in the midnight darkness. He would tell us of the long journey it had and how important it was that it reached its destination.

It was not until I was an adult that my mother told me my father did care about my every move in life I made, watching me secretly and only assisting me when it was absolutely necessary. After walking me to my kindergarten class for a week, he followed me a few days clandestinely to make sure I got there safely. Whenever I came to him with tears riding my eyelid as a boy, he would take his hands, big as shovels, cup my face in them, and say, holding his face close to mine and smiling all the time, "You are on a journey boy...you are on a journey!" almost always biting my cheek softly before walking away. He was strong; he was so big.

Upon awakening the next morning, my prelude to preparing for another day was to look in on my distressed

Hospice for a Snowbird

visitor, who had moved from the gable to the window near my mother's bedroom, looking off into the distance as if giving homage to the sun as it crept above the treetops. I was meticulous that morning, fearing a noise from me might disrupt my honored guest's equanimity. I was a feather in my office also that night, daring not to make a sound as my visitor rested, now walking across the whiteness of the snow that had fallen that afternoon while I was away. It was indeed stronger, with its great head held high by its long and gracile neck, its great wings and body hunched over its large webbed feet, oblivious, uncaring of the coldness of the snow, staring into the north, seeming to contemplate the snow that would approach viciously as the season grew colder and which I also knew would come.

The next morning a sound brought me from my sleep to the window of my office. At a distance I stood to watch, my visitor from the night sky open its great wings of gargantuan size into the wind that blew its coldness into them. It stepped down the tarred roof, honking with its deep honk. Its great and strong lungs inhaled the air that worked its great heart that would drive its great self on to the south until the cold became the warmth of the gulf. I knew it was strong.

I wondered if it would stop for a rest and repast in the mountains of smoke in North Carolina; or would its great wings take it to visit Faulkner's Mississippi, on to the quagmire of Louisiana, or maybe on to Texas? Would it be willing to take a message to my father's stone in Texas, telling him I am stronger because of him? That like this Great Bird, with wings so great, so vast, I would not, have not fallen to the vicissitudes of life.

It worked its great feathered wings up and down while stepping down an imaginary runway I saw, compelling the powdered snow to form eddies beneath them, beating them until they lifted its hugeness off the blackness of the tar, then descending its bulk again to touch with its large webbed feet.

Memoirs of a Taxi Driver

Reversing its direction, it ran towards my window with wings outstretched, quickly reversed its direction a second time to meet the wind that took its greatness and brought its bulk to bear upon it, lifting it higher into the morning chillness, becoming a microscopic organism far from me in the distant sky, each great sweep of its great wings taking it higher, farther away from me! South, south it flew to meet the warmth of the Gulf Breeze!

With My Strong Hand

A woman has power; a woman has influence. Open a history book and you will see where whole empires and kingdoms have been given up for the love of a woman. Open a newspaper, the advertisement in the first few pages are directed at the eyes of a woman in most circumstances. Women have influence; they have power in the world. They can make a man strong in his heart; they can make a man weak in his soul.

One night I had driven my taxi into the early morning hours, and there was another taxi driver sitting on a bench in the garage after I had parked my car. I had seen him around before, but I had never spoken to him. He was an ugly man, and one of his hands was deformed from birth it seemed. When I set down next to him he paid me no attention, and when I asked him how his business had been that shift, with an accent he told me it had been good. Just as I was about to rise and walk away after counting my money, he started to talk to me, as a tape recorder might start if a button was pressed on it accidentally. I set myself back down to listen to him over my right shoulder.

"The place that I have come from, in the summer months it can become very hot. At night, the temperature, at times,

51

can get close to freezing. My people did not have homes as in this country. They had homes that were made from the bush that grew in the desert. When we built those places they were not forever as they are here. They were for a few days or for a season. After some time had passed, we left them for the desert to claim, and we moved on to other places.

"My people considered themselves to be the true people. We were the real people in the world. We had lived in my country for thousands of years, long before the Hereros and the Tswanas came to take and farm our land. We lived a simple life. The food we ate was the food that the land provided. We did not grow crops as you do in this country. We moved about to harvest foods that grew around us, and we hunted the animals that grazed the land.

"At night my people did not travel about. Lions, hyenas, snakes, and other wild beasts were walking the land, and it could be dangerous for my people. It was rare that animals attacked us, but when an attack did occur, it was talked about for a long time and not forgotten. Because of that, we usually traveled about in the day and stayed in our small villages at night. We felt safer there; we had each other there. That is the way we lived long before I was born to my land.

"When I was born to my parents, they already had two children that ate the steenbok. My sister was still at my mother's breast, and my mother did not want my sister to spoil the milk for me, and it is because of that she decided to place me in the ground with the digging stick that she took with her to the tree outside our small village. After she had given birth to me only a few feet outside our small village, she began to dig the hole to place me in. When I was born, I was not a complete child as you can see, my right hand has three important fingers missing, and because of that, my mother dug faster to place the dirt over me. As my mother worked the ground to place me in forever, her heart became soft for me, because my face was her face and my eyes were her eyes, and she took me back to the huts that made our village.

"As I grew into a child who ran through the sand, I saw my hand was different from those of the other children, and they saw that to also be the case. They would not let that difference lay quiet when tempers grew hot like the fire my people cooked the gemsbok over. They tormented me about my difference. I was not a handsome one either, I was ugly; I grew to know that.

"As I came to the age to take a wife, I was shy and far away from the females in talk. They did not want me, my hand was not right, my belly hung from me, and my butt was too big they said. I got by, but it was difficult.

"My family arranged a marriage for me with a girl in another village far from my own, but after many months and almost two years added to that, the girl refused me and her skin crawled like the caterpillar with disgust for me. She would not even let me lay with her in our hut. She left me many times, and in the end, the marriage did not work, and I left for my village and my family.

"There was one girl who was beautiful like only the hand of God could make in the world. I felt that she was too far above me, and I did not look her way. She was married to a Zhun/twa from the south. They had two children, one girl that walked and a small boy that she carried at her hip. When her husband died it was from a sickness that started in his chest that would not let him go. His brother was a healer. He tried to cure him, but God had placed a spiritual arrow in him, and he passed into the Shadow World.

"My wife loved her first husband and did not do well without him and sat in mourning quite a long time. She cried and cried until she herself became ill and only recovered after some months of protest from her family. Many suitors came to her with proposals of marriage, but she turned them away from her. However, there was one Zhun/twa that came again and again until she changed her thoughts. They lived together for a long time until he left for some reason. My heart was with that woman, and I went to her with the meat from the eland that walks across our land and tried to sway her to me. She laughed at me. I was not complete she would tell me. My belly hung out away from me, and my butt was too big.

"She moved from our village with her family when the dry summer heat came and finally moved to the east to do work for the Tswanas. When word came to me of her place, I too went to the Tswanas for work and to look upon her. I placed my hut next to hers, and when I hunted the animals, I placed the meat at her hut. She would thank me with a laugh, but I was not a complete man, so she only kept my company because of my efforts.

"I wanted to marry her, but she would not marry me. Even her family pushed her to that thing, but she refused me. I worked for her and loved her children, and when her son was able to walk on the sand I made toys for him to play with. Even the Tswana headman told her she should marry me, but she refused me under any circumstances. However, in time, under pressure from neighbors and family, she reluctantly married me. When she became angry with me, she would tell me she only married me to make her family quiet with their words of insistence.

"I was proud to be with her. When I walked with her my heart was strong; my chest was proud, and my spirit was well. But understand me, her heart was not complete for me, and when I was away she took lovers into our hut, and when I would find them sitting together, they would only say they were talking. When I complained, she would use words with fire in them to say my suspicions were false and that I was an ugly man anyway.

"We moved away from the Tswanas and lived in the bush with her mother who was a sick one in her old age. It is there that we lived and lived for some time. A time came that I had to leave and work with the Tswanas. I was away for some months, and on my return my wife's belly was swollen with child. I asked her how it would be that when I

With My Strong Hand

left the moon was upon her, but on my return she could be with child. Her words were fire, and she did not stop for hours until I sat quiet at the campfire.

"We lived on and on until her belly became very big, and when the child did come it did not move, and my wife was far from me in her thoughts. She blamed me for its loss, and as it can be between a man and woman, it was a cold thing between us for a long time.

"Word came to me that my mother was sick and dying, and we all packed to leave for the west. We traveled all that day and slept that night and traveled all the next day and slept the next night. On the third day we traveled until the sun became too hot and rested and traveled again as the sun went away.

"On our arrival my mother had died, and my tears did not stop from my eyes. I knew she had gone when my brother saw me, and met us at a distance. His eyes had no peace in them. We lived and lived in my mother's village until it came time to return to the east for the work that waited at the Tswana settlement.

"My wife was never satisfied. She complained on the way to my mother's village and on the way back to our village at the Tswana settlement.

"Some months later word came to me that my father would be ill. I told my wife to pack for our trip back to my father's village. She refused me and would not go with me. I left without her and the children, and I went upon my way to my father's place. When I reached him, my bother had been in a trance for him, had stopped the blood he coughed up, and he sat up better in his hut. I stayed with my father along with my brother, and we hunted and took care of him until we were sure he was completely well, and I left for my wife and family in the east.

"On my return, my children ran to meet me, for they knew my walk at a distance. As you already know, they were not my children between my wife and I but from her first marriage. But I had a heart for them that was complete as it

55

would be for my own children. When I was away from them my heart would ache for them, and my mind would not leave them. And they both looked like my wife, and they had a step like her step as she walked along the bush land.

"Again, on my return, my wife was with child, and I had not laid with her many months, and I asked how it could be that she was pregnant with a child, and I was not there to be with her. She did not speak to me, and when I continued, she became a wild woman with her mouth so loud, to remind me that I was not a complete man, I was ugly, that I was nothing, that my belly stuck out from me, and my butt was too big. I only sat inside the hut with my soul weak in me, to look at the sun go from the sky.

"We lived and lived until the baby did come, and when that child came into the world it did not look like me, as I knew it would not. I hunted for it as I did all the children, and when it cried it came to me and I loved it, as it would be mine. But in my land, not all children live until they can grow to take their first steps, and after one year, that child became sick inside and died. I had tears in my eyes, and my mine did not leave that child that my heart had grown to be complete for.

"My wife, she did blame me for that child's death, but not with the heart that a woman would if she knew it to be true. I loved that child, and she knew it.

"We lived on in the bush. She was angry about many things that wife of mine. When there was no response from me, she would beat me with things that might lie around. And it did come to be that she would throw things that might lie around also. She once took a stone when I did not look her way and threw it to make me not see the sun for some hours. When I did return with my senses it was the nighttime, and I lay were I had fallen with her not in our hut. There was no sorrow in her heart for me on her return, and I did not provoke her with questions or complaints. My heart was complete for that woman and her children. I

With My Strong Hand

needed them all. I knew I was ugly in the world; no one else would have me.

"Secretly, the boy was my favorite child. However, I was careful not to let that be known to my daughter and others. He was like no other boy that I could know. He was never in one place, and my eyes were always alert to any danger that he might get into. As a boy of five, I do think he could run and jump high like the gemsbok. He was strong and fast for his age, and his mind was always asking questions that I found to be difficult to answer. He could be rough like the hyena in play with his sister but a good listener as he sat on his hunches to watch me work. He looked like his mother completely, and as I said, even his walk was her walk with ever month and year that came and went, but in a boyish way. I can never forget him. I can feel him in my arms now, so small, so warm. I would carry him about on my shoulders. He would hold tightly with his fingers at my hair; he would laugh with happiness.

"To that boy I wanted to be a real father. I wanted to show him the way to manhood. He did not care that I was ugly. And when tears came to his eyes he would come to my arms and only care about that moment and not my ugly face. I had plans for him and his sister. There might be a better life for them than that of the bush. Maybe, just maybe, they could learn from the books of the world that the Hereros and some Tswanas knew about. But they were not really my children. I would have had to hear my wife's words about my thoughts.

"My right hand is not a complete hand and my strength lies in my left hand. It is a fast hand, a very, very, strong hand, and correct, like that of the eagle in its strike.

"I can kill a man with my left hand. Killing does happen everywhere in the world and my people are no different than the people in the world when it comes to killing. When discrepancies occur, the other members of the village will separate the two warring parties until tempers have cooled. However, poison arrows are used on occasion and some

Memoirs of a Taxi Driver

times innocent people are struck. There is no antidote for the wound from a poison arrow in my country, and it is rare if one recovers.

"When a fight does turn fatal, the perpetrator will move away from the area, far from the place of conflict and live a normal life. It has been that way for thousands of years in my country. But if fatalities become a pattern by that one perpetrator or the perpetrator becomes dangerous, he is killed.

"My real trouble in my life began after working some months in the north. I had come back tired with the sand on my body to find a man and my wife sitting together in our hut. When I came to the huts opening, my wife threw wood at me to keep me on the outside with angry sounds from her. She instructed me to take our children from her sister's hut and to bring them back to our hut, and I did not do that for I was tired, and a man sat in the hut that was our hut. I only sat by the fire not happy inside myself.

"I heard them making the sounds of a husband and wife in our hut, and I could not understand that woman to do that thing with me in our camp without fear. I went to her sister's hut and spoke out loud that a sister of hers was making the sound of a wife with another man as her husband sat outside.

"Her sister went to our hut and asked how could it be that a strange man could be in the hut that was her husband's hut with his wife and that his wife would be making the sounds of a wife with a man while the husband was outside the hut.

"When her sister had spoken those words in my wife's presence, my wife came from the hut in a roar to me. She shouted words at me, accused me of spying on her, came close to me, and kicked me in my back as I sat near the fire. That kick had some spiritual poison in it and made my heart weak for her. And when that brought no words from me, she used words against my mother who rested in the Shadow World. From there she hurt me and made me feel ashamed in front of the man who smiled near our hut and

58

the other neighbors that stood and sat close by. My soul became weak inside me. I wanted to be a good husband to that woman, but that woman was empty inside her heart for me, and I was ashamed.

"After I had finished my work there, I picked myself up and ran away from my people. Now I am here in this city alone with only my memories of my people and the past I left behind."

I asked him why he had run, what had happen to his family?

"My wife's sister came to push my wife away from me and to tell my wife that was not the way to treat a husband. My wife argued with her sister for some time and came to me again to kick at me. When I only sat there, she came close to me again and kicked me in my back into the hot coals, for I was tired and had little strength, and my strong hand, my good hand became burnt.

"My voice was loud with pain around the people that heard me. My mind was not with me, and I lifted myself from the fire to place my strong hand around her throat like the speed of the cobra to squeeze the breath from her body as her feet hung above the ground. Her eyes grew large from her head, I felt the bone in her neck crack under my hand, and I dashed her to the stones on the ground.

"With one motion I took a spear and thrust it through the Zhun/twa as he came to rescue her until its sharp head came from his back into the open air, and I beat him with my fists until he did not stand above the ground."

A True Story

Far to the south, through the forest of the Congo, west of the Serengeti to the east, and into the desert, sits a village in the evening sunset. In this village are a people that are the last of their kind. They have been left alone by the people of the outside, primarily because of their remoteness to the rest of the world. All around them the planes and roads grow ever closer to them, and plans are being made without their knowledge to move them away to a government-funded community. Some minerals of importance have been found nearby in the ground.

The village consists of five or six grass huts, and the people mingle about to prepare for the darkness that will come after the sun has finally set for the day.

Three small girls laugh and play not far from an old man who has known the land before the planes and trucks made their sounds overhead and nearby.

One little girl lifts herself up after being pushed down by her friend and looks over to the old man sitting crossed-legged in front of his hut with his wife gone from the earth a long time. She approaches him and speaks with her girl voice:

"Grandfather, tell us the true story of Kumsa and Tasa again."

A True Story

"I told you the story two days ago little one."

"Please tell it again Grandfather; I want my two friends over there to hear the words."

The old man sitting by his hut sees two small girls materialize into his failing eyesight, to stand closer to the campfire.

"I am hungry little girl, put that duiker foot on the coals, and let it cook itself as I tell the story."

The small girls collect themselves around the fire on their hunches and peer up at the old man as he sits across from them. He places his hands at his temples with the palms facing the girls and opens his eyes wide to bring smiles to the faces of the children.

"A long, long time ago, before you were born—"

"Grandfather, tell us the good part first."

"The story will not be good if I do not start from the beginning, child. Be quiet, and let an old man tell the story."

As he says that and has the attention of the children, some of the adults who sit about the camp and have heard the true love story told to them by their parents as children, come closer and sit down to join the children around the early evening campfire.

"A long, long time ago, before there were trucks and planes, before our land was taken from us, before you were born, before my father was born, before his grandfather was born, before ten or fifteen of our great, great grandfathers were born, there was a boy named Kumsa and a girl named Tasa who was very lovely. Kumsa was the son of Gau and his wife Bey. Tasa was the daughter of Bo and his wife Twah. They both lived in villages that were apart from one another. They grew up apart at first. They did not know one another until the day Kumsa's parents, moving about to find the water that is scarce doing the dry season, stopped in the village of Tasa's parents.

"It was hot on that day. Kumsa and Tasa were only about eight or nine-years-old at that time, but when they saw one another they became friends right away and could not leave

61

themselves apart. Also in that village were Dem and Kashe. They were bad boys and would fight anyone who would stand in their way. They were bigger than all the other children, and when they saw Kumsa playing with Tasa, they tried to hit him with their hands and the things that lay about the village. But Kumsa was unafraid and fought Dem and Kashe and beat them to the ground, and Dem and Kashe ran from Kumsa. But every chance they got, they would try to fight Kumsa, but Kumsa was brave and would always win against Dem and Kashe in a fight.

"Kumsa and Tasa would play all the day long, and when other children would come to play with them, they would not play with them as children would play. They lived in their own world, played husband and wife and seemed to understand one another like children in this world cannot understand one another. They would run together through the village and only play between themselves, and no hour would pass without them being together.

"At night when each family went apart to sleep in their own huts, Kumsa and Tasa would stand together before parting and speak in low voices as adults would and part with heavy hearts to their separate huts. And in the morning when the women would go to the groves to collect the nin berries and mongongo nuts, Kumsa and Tasa would harvest together as adults would while the other children would run and play about, as children do.

"When it came time for Gau and Bey to move on to the east, where their families lived, Kumsa would not leave with them for the east. He said, 'My mother, my father who have held me and fed me, I can not leave Tasa, I feel her heart in me and she feels my heart in her, and I can not leave her.' And his mother said to him, 'Kumsa, son of mine, you are crazy in your head; you will come with us to our families to the east. They wait for us now. Come out of your crazy head and come.'

"When Tasa saw that Kumsa was to leave, she stood by her parents and said to them, 'My mother, my father who

A True Story

have held me and fed me, do not let the father and mother of Kumsa take him away from this place, I feel his heart in me and he feels my heart in him, do not let them take Kumsa from me.' And her mother said to her, 'My daughter, you are a child, one who does not know the world yet. Get this crazy talk out of your head. Let Kumsa go home to his family, and you stay here and play with your friends that are about the place.'

"Dem and Kashe who were at their side in play, stopped their play and said, 'Yes, Kumsa should go with his parents. We do not want him here. Kumsa is a bad boy and should stay away from here.' And Tasa said to them as an adult would say, 'You boys are bad. Go away from this place I talk to my parents. You are silly boys. Go away from this place. You are jealous of Kumsa.'

"That talk with their parents did not stop their parents, and Gau and Bey took Kumsa away to the east, and Tasa stayed with her parents in their camp.

"Some years passed after that time, and one day Kumsa and his parents came again through the village of Tasa, and again those two children could not be separated, and they played, talked together as adults, and in the morning before the sun became too hot, Kumsa would leave with his father to hunt and Tasa would leave with her mother for the groves to gather as our people have always done.

"On their return, there was always Dem and Kashe who caused trouble for them. Dem and Kashe never wanted to grow-up, and they would torment Kumsa, and Kumsa would fight them, because Kumsa was not afraid of them, and he beat them down to the ground. Tasa would say to them, 'One day I will marry Kumsa. He will be my husband, and I will be his wife. And we will live together in our hut. No woman will marry you Kashe, no woman will marry you Dem. Go away from here and leave us alone.'

"And sure as the sun came everyday, Kumsa and Tasa were married, and they lived in their hut together and the childish play and jealousy of Dem and Kashe left them.

They all would live in the same village together when the rains would come but move apart when the rains would stop.

"Times were different then. The Hereors would come upon our land to fight us and take from us.

"One day, while Kumsa, Kashe, and Dem were out hunting, the Hereros came and raided their village and took the women and children.

"Some of the men had been out hunting for three days, and some were out visiting other villages, and on their return the men in a rush came together to follow the tracks of the Hereors that led to the west.

"They sent word to other villages, and other men came to help because some of the women and children were relatives.

"There were twenty, thirty men in pursuit of the Hereros. The men walked and walked until they had left their land and were in a place that was not their own. There was a storm that lasted two days with the sand blowing all about and wiping away the trail.

"The men searched for two weeks to find the trail of the Hereros and the women they had stolen from their village. Some men stopped and went home, others turned back later until it was only Dem, Kumsa, and Kashe and ten other Zhun/twasi. They went on into the desert where no plants grew in the sand to follow the trail. Just when there was no hope, Kumsa with his keen eyes found the trail, and the men continued on across the desert until they came to the remnants of a Herero campsite.

"It was an old site, but it belonged to the Hereros who had stolen their loved ones.

"So, the men went off to the west for many days following the trail of the Hereors through the dry land of the desert, to only lose them again, when the wind came from the sky to blow away the trail.

"Some men wanted to turn back, but Dem, Kumsa, and Kashe, with the play of childhood gone from them, spoke to

A True Story

the men as elders and encouraged them to continue on to the west, and the men did continue to the west.

"After a few days, they found the trail and the main village of the Hereros.

"That village was to the west and to the north of where we sit now, and the land was strange and different, and in the village there were too many Hereros for the few Zhun/twasi who had pursued them, and the Zhun/twasi sat outside the village and thought of what to do.

"There was no way that they could go into the village to save the women during the day, So Dem, Kumsa and Kashe with the others decided to go into the village in the night to steal the women and escape to their village.

"It took a long time of hiding in the desert and planning to rescue the women. Many nights Kumsa would cry for Tasa. His heart was in her, and her heart was in him, and when they were apart from one another they were not complete.

"One day, when their plans were almost completed, many Hereors came upon them in the desert and chased them away from their village farther to the west. They pursued them for many days until they came upon a large body of water.

"That body of water was like no water a Zhun/twa had ever seen. It was bigger than all the land around us, and when the men came upon it, they did not know how to go through it.

"They ran along the land that the water came up on to escape the Hereros. On they went until the wind began to blow with the Hereors behind them. The wind and water was blowing like a Zhun/twa had never seen with the Hereors only a few feet behind the Zhun/twasi.

"Suddenly, a big wave came up upon the shore to take the Hereors and the Zhun/twasi off the land into the water. The water took them out into its big waves and brought them back to shore again. And then picked them all up again and took them back out into it big waves again.

Memoirs of a Taxi Driver

"The water thrashed them all until the night was finished, and in the morning all the Hereors were dead and only five Zhun/twasi were alive, laid back upon the land by the great water or by swimming to the shore.

"There were many bodies on the shore and some in the water away from the shore.

"Dem and Kashe were among the five Zhun/twasi who had survived, and they looked for the other Zhun/twasi who might have survived. Some of the bodies were out in the water away from the shore, and they looked hard for Kumsa.

"They saw Kumsa away from the shore but could not swim to him, for the great water took him away into its great vastness.

"Kashe said that it was Kumsa, and Dem said that it was not Kumsa who floated in the great water. They waited for some days along with the others for the water to return the dead Zhun/twasi, but the water never returned them to the shore. They searched up and down the land along the water, but the water did not place the Zhun/twasi were they could find them.

"Kashe, Dem, and the others were very brave and would not leave without the women and children who had been stolen from their village. They went back to the place of the Hereros and waited for their chance to steal back the women, and after many weeks and much planning they went into the village at night and took the women and children away, along with Tasa, and ran back through the desert for many weeks to their village.

"Tasa asked about Kumsa, and Dem told her that Kumsa had been taken away by a great water that lay to the west, a water that was greater than any water that ever existed, water that did not taste like the water that they would drink but tasted like salt when it was at the tongue. Tasa started to cry and would not go on. She told all the Zhun/twasi that she would go back to that place of the water that they spoke of to find Kumsa. Maybe they were mistaken and Kumsa

66

was not taken away into the vastness of the water to be lost forever.

"She started to leave, but Dem would not let her leave and told her that she was out of her head with craziness. Even the others did not, could not talk sense into her head, and she started to the west across the desert to the water that they had described.

"They all told her that the Hereors would get her or some wild animal would eat her, but Tasa's heart was Kumsa's heart, and Kumsa's heart was Tasa's heart, and no one could stop her, and she walked into the desert towards the water that they had spoken of.

"Kashe and Dem were brave as Kumsa was once brave, and they followed Tasa into the desert to take her to the place where they had been taken away by the water. After many days they came upon that water that was bigger than any water that a Zhun/twa had ever seen, and they all looked upon it to find Kumsa, and Kumsa could not be found. Tasa insisted that they walk up and down the land that the water touched to make sure the water had not released Kumsa.

"After some days it was hopeless, and Tasa started to cry. She sat five days, and the tears would not leave her, and she cried some more until she became sick. Kashe and Dem scolded her, and told her if she did not stop crying and leave, she would die or the Hereros would come to find them, kill them, and take her away.

"Slowly, they persuaded her to leave, and they walked across the desert to their village that was many weeks from them, and Tasa would not stop crying, and in her heart she was lost.

"Many weeks and months passed, and she was sad and set herself apart from the others and would not eat and could not sleep. Her family scolded her and nursed her until finally Tasa began to recover.

"Tasa was very beautiful. Dem and all the other men in her village and all the other men in the villages around

Memoirs of a Taxi Driver

wanted to marry her, but she would not marry anyone, and the years went away, and she still would not marry.

"Dem went to her many times with his words of marriage, and Tasa knew he was a good provider with his bow and arrows, but Tasa would not look upon him as a husband, and time went by.

"Her family scolded her for walking away from a man as good as Dem. They pressured her and tormented her. Even Kumsa's mother and father went to her and said, 'It has been ten dry seasons since Kumsa has last set down with us, maybe it would be good for you to marry Dem. Kumsa, I am sure, would want it to be that way. Marry Dem, walk with him and have children so that they can bring joy into your life.'

"Finally, Tasa married Dem. She cared for Dem, but not as she had for Kumsa. Dem was the best hunter in their village, and he was more handsome than all the other men, but her heart was never his heart. They did laugh together and play together, but it was not the same as it had been with Kumsa.

"The years passed, until five dry seasons and five rainy seasons had come and gone.

"One morning, as the sun came up from the east, the village slowly came awake. The people rose to sit outside their huts to bring back to life the coals at their fires.

"Kumsa's mother was up early in front of her fire, and she stroke it to turn the coals and placed a fagot upon it to nourish it to life.

"Tasa set at her mother's hut talking to her with sleep in her face, and Dem came out of their hut to sit on his hunches to speak with Kashe who had gotten up earlier and was walking into the camp with a springhare he had trapped.

"In the village there were some who were awake but more who were still asleep.

"As Kumsa's mother stroke the fire that was in front of her, she looked up and in the distance she saw the figure of

A True Story

a man coming towards the village. It was not close enough to be that of a man, but it came on through the morning mist to have legs as a man, and arms of that of a man, but it could have been a mistake that her eyes played upon her.

"She stood up and dropped the fagot in her hand that was now afire and called to her husband with excitement, 'Gau husband of mind, leave your sleep and come from our hut.'

"She called to Dem and Tasa without moving her eyes from the figure that moved towards them, 'Dem, Tasa, who are now married and sleep together at night in the same hut, come to me now to see this thing that an old woman would see to make it clear to her.'

"'My eyes and mind are not wrong inside of me, I see Kumsa coming.' Her husband rose from his stump and looked at the man that was still too far away to make him clear to be any kind of man at all and said, 'Woman, you are old, your mind and eyes are not young as they once were. That is not Kumsa.'

"The woman took a few steps away from the hut as a mother would who had longed for a son's return, and each step had anticipation and hope.

"'It is Kumsa I tell you, I know his step, his body leans to the right and his arms move behind him as he walks. It is Kumsa! It is Kumsa I tell you!'

"The old woman, with her old bones took a few more steps forward to bring her eyes closer to the figure, and Tasa stepped forward away from her mother, who paid no attention to the figure as it twisted and turned through the sand and shrubs and impressions of the desert to come closer to the village.

"Tasa beckoned Dem with her voice and finger, 'Dem, Dem it is Kumsa. Dem, it is Kumsa!' Dem rose from his stump and peeked around his hut to see the man as he became visible. 'What is wrong with you, woman that I am married to? Kumsa is dead. That is not Kumsa. Kumsa is no more. The great water took him away; I saw it with my own eyes.'

Memoirs of a Taxi Driver

"The women, not listening to him, started to walk toward the figure, and as they came closer, their walks became trots, and then they broke into a run and ran into the man's arms and he embraced them, and they screamed and jumped around him, not screams of torment or of fright but of joy. And as the others heard that commotion, they all rose from whatever they were doing and stood or walked closer to the figures, and it was Kumsa, it was Kusma who had come from out of the Shadow World and through the desert into their village.

"Tasa and Bey hung onto the figure for a long time with tears coming out of themselves, and they ran their hands over his face and over his body until they knew that it was really Kumsa. They did that for a long time until slowly and unbeknownst to themselves, they had walked the distance to the village and the people who awaited them and where Tasa fainted in Kumsa's arms.

"With Tasa in his arms, Kumsa came into the village to see his father standing before him and the others standing-- some he had known and others who were new to his eyes. He spoke to his father, 'Father, I am Kumsa, your son. Do not be afraid of me. I have come from across the great water that took me away from my family and my land.'

"'How can it be that you have come back? It was told to me that a great body of water took you into its stomach away from the land, and for many days and weeks you did not come back out of it.'

"'Father, I am your son, and I have come from that great water.' The old man walked up to his son and placed his hand at his face to make sure that it was really Kumsa. It was Kumsa, and he then touched his neck and body to make his mind believed that it was Kumsa.

"'Stop, my husband, take our son and make him comfortable. I will bring mongongo nuts and springhare for our son to eat. Take him, take him and sit with him.'

A True Story

"Dem and Kashe stood at a distance in disbelief. Dem walked over to the people that surrounded Kumsa and took Tasa from his arms.

"'I am Dem. I am the one who saw the great water take you away from the land. How is it that you have come back from its stomach?'

"'Yes Dem it is I, I am Kumsa, the one you used to fight and play with. The Great Spirit did save me, and I have come back from the stomach of the great water that took me away from my family and our land.'

"Bey came to sit next to Gau, Tasa, and Kumsa. She handed Kumsa some nuts, the leg of a springhare, and water. He consumed it to feed an empty stomach.

"'Let my son rest with his family, he has come a long way. Let him eat and drink. He is tired. Sit down Dem; sit down Kashe. Everyone sit down. My son has come home.'

"Some set themselves down slowly, as they would around a spirit that had come back from the Shadow World. It was something that they could not believe. It was impossible for one to come from out of the darkness of the Shadow World, and the word spread around the village that Kumsa was not the Kumsa that they had known but a spirit from the Shadow World who had come to bring death and destruction upon them.

"Kumsa finished his meal happily and wiped his mouth with his wrist as he had as a child. His mother leaned into his shoulder with her temple and still crying, Tasa knelt behind him with her arms wrapped around his neck.

"Kumsa hurriedly, with a smile and hands told everyone to sit down so that he could tell them the story of how he had survived the great water that had taken him away. Some of the Zhun/twasi sat and some of them stood, not sure if he would jump up and bring havoc upon them.

"Kumsa took one last swallow of water, and he began.

"'It is I, Kumsa; the one whom you fed and played with as a child. I am the son of Gau and Bey. I came from their bodies, and you must know that I am Kumsa, the one that

71

you knew before we went to steal our women back from the Hereros who are our enemies.

"'It was Kashe, Dem, and other Zhun/twasi who ran across the land by my side to pursue the Hereors. It was I, along with them who sat outside the village of the Hereors to make plans to steal our women and children back, and it was I, along with them, who ran from the Hereors along the great water that took us away into its stomach.

"'It is true that the great water took me away from the land. I had swallowed much of the body of the water into my stomach, and I did not know my mind. I lay asleep in a dark world, and when the light came to my eyes I was being taken away by the water, and there was no land to walk on. I was lost, and I was alone.

"'I prayed to the Great Spirit that we all know to save me, but I did not know if that would happen, and I was carried along for many days until I lost my senses to the world around me again, and I awoke one day inside a large floating branch, made of many branches that would take all the branches in our land to make, and people stood around and worked around it to keep it afloat and headed in the right direction.

"'Those people who had pulled me from the great water were like we are, with hands and feet to carry them, but they spoke words that I or you could not understand, and their skin was white, and their noses were long and pointed like the beak of a bird, and their eyes were in their heads with different colors.

"'They gave me water that was fresh, and they gave me food that was bad to the taste but which I ate because my stomach was hungry inside of me. It tasted bad, but I ate that food, and when I finished that food, I asked for more in my words, but they did not know my words, and I did not know their words, but with my hand to my mouth they understood and gave me more of the food that tasted badly.

"'When I became stronger, I walked around that thing that the men worked on to learn how it moved about the water.

A True Story

After all my strength had finally come back to me, they let me work on the thing that carried us through the water. They did not understand me when I told them that I had to find my wife, and we sailed south until the water became very big, and many times our vessel almost went below the water, and when we ran short of water to drink, we brought the vessel close to the land, and we collected fresh water and met people whom I had never seen before, people who were friendly and some that were not so friendly, and we barely escaped with our lives.

"'We then turned and headed north along the coast until we came to a rain forest where a people prayed to a god that they called Allah, and from there we went farther across the great water that took us to a people who called themselves Hindu. For some years we were there, and we traded with those people, and left that place to make our way back to where I had been found.

"'I asked in their language, as I had learned their language, if I could go back to my land, for I was married, and my mother and father were only a week and a few days across the desert, but the headman on the vessel that carried us across the water would not allow me to touch the land, but he kept me with him until we came to his home land that was the place that he had been born.

"'In that place I saw many vessels like the one that I was on. There were more of those vessels than any Zhun/twa could count, and I was lost amongst them, and I did not know that place, and it was a cold place that had rain that turned white in the cold and stuck to the ground, and one would have to wear animal skin over one's feet to keep them dry and warm.

"'In their land, they took all the goods that they had collected to their headman that was the headman over all the headmen. And he gave them instructions and praise for the work that they had done.

"'During my time there, I did not see or find any one who looked like me, and people would come to me and touch my

73

Memoirs of a Taxi Driver

skin in surprise, because it was rare that some one of my kind was amongst them, and it was not until we were to go on another mission across the great water that I did see some people with my darkness coming onto the land, and when I tried to speak to them I did not know their words, and they did not know my words as they went by me in chains and yokes that were around their necks.

"'After two cold seasons, I, my headman, and others who were to work upon the vessel, left again for the foreign places. We went south until we came to the Ibo people. We took on fresh water, food, and went down along the rain forest until we came to the land of the Hereors that I knew by its desert and sand, and I asked my headman if I could go back to my land. I told him that my wife was not far off and that my heart was her heart and her heart was my heart, and he told me that I could not go back to my land, and we went by my land, and my heart was sad inside of me, and we went down past the Cape and north again until we spoke and walked with the Muslims and on to the land of the Hindus.

"'On that voyage we went farther until we came to a land where the people made silk from worms and ate all their food with sticks and ate a white grain, as we eat the mongongo nuts, with every kind of food. Their food was good to the taste and easy on the stomach.

"'From that land we left across the sea and a great storm came upon us and brought us to a land where the people were different from any people we had met. They were very kind and very clean. And all the people would come to me and touch my skin in disbelief, when I allowed them, and when I did not, they would stand off and secretly admire the skin of a Zhun/twa.

"'While we were at that land, the earth would shake. And when the earth would shake, our bodies would shake, and all the things that they had built would shake and sometimes come down to the ground. After we had traded with those people, we came from their land and went about our way

A True Story

back to the home city of Lisbon that my headman was from, a city bigger than all the huts of all the Zhun/twa that have ever lived in our land since the beginning of time.

"'We went by the Hindus, and we sailed by the Muslims, on south around the Cape, and when we came to the land of the Hereors, which I had known as my enemies, I asked my headman if I could go home to my people. I told him that I had served him well and that my wife, more beautiful than all the women, in all the places that we had visited, was not far off and that my heart inside of me would not work without pain away from her, and he told me that I could not go home to my people, and my heart was heavy inside of me, and we sailed north past the Ibos passed Gibraltar to the east and on to Lisbon.

"'It was there that I lived until the snow had come and gone twice, and after we had rested and had made repairs to our ship, we made ready to leave again.

"'I was a seaman. I knew the sea, the people thereabouts the coast, and the land that the sea came upon.

"'We moved down along the coast, never really leaving the land, past the rain forest, and down along the land that I knew that the Hereors walked on.

"'I did not ask my headman if I could go home but watched the land that would take me to my people slowly go pass me, but in my mind I had made a plan that in the night I would lower myself into the water and swim to shore and walk the distance to my father that is Gau, my mother that is Bey, and my wife that my heart is inside of.

"'After I had done that, the water would not let me reach the land, it took me away from the land. My life I knew would leave me if I did not fight the great water as a Zhun/twa. I swam with great strength for a long time. When there was no more strength in me, I continued on across the water with the heart of Tasa in my every stroke.

"'When I reached the shore, the life was not in me to move for one day, and after that one day I moved farther above the shore into the sand and rested one more day. And after I had eaten the lizard and dug the water to drink, I was ready to cross the sand.

"'Across the sand I did go until I came to the bush, and not one day did I stop until I have just come upon your faces.'

"Dem, not sitting throughout the story said, 'You can not expect us to believe that story. You are not Kumsa. Kashe and other Zhun/twasi saw the great water take you away from the land. It was Kumsa that I saw with his face in the water. There are no lands in the world but this land, and we are the only true people.'

"'I am Kumsa. I am the one who ran and played with you and Kashe as a child. It is you and I who found the beehive in the termite mound that the honey badger had eaten but not finished. Remember, I told you not to eat the honey, and after you had eaten the honey, the honey badger's spirit got into you, and you became sick and could not walk.

"'Is it not true that I had to carry you on my back to our village and that you were sick in your chest for many days and that my uncle who is a healer with his own hands brought you back from the Shadow World that would have taken you without his help. If I am not Kumsa, how do I know those things Dem?'

"'Did you not make this mark at my wrist with a sharp stone that you threw at me and cut the flesh deep down to the white flesh. And after that was done, did I not knock you down to the ground and kick you in the stomach in your grandmother's village? If I am not Kumsa, how do I know those things?'

"'Yes, Kumsa did do those things, but Kumsa is dead. His spirit lies in the Shadow World, and you are not Kumsa. I saw Kumsa with his body and face in the great water, and I saw that great water take him away.'

"'Kashe, look at me, I am Kumsa to you. One day while at the mongongo grove with our parents, did not we find a baby ant bear with almost no hair upon it and skin like that of a human. Did we not kill it, and that night we ate it, and

A True Story

while telling how we had killed it, you said that you had killed it, and I had said that I had killed it, and we fought with words over it for a long time, and because of that we were not friends for a long time over it? Was it not me who saw the cobra at the well that you almost stepped on?

"'Was it not me that saw, with my own eyes, that danger that your foot came close to?'

"Another Zhun/twa spoke out, 'There are no people with white faces. There has never in the world been faces like those you speak of. There is no branch that is so big that it can carry men around on it. You are a demon who has come from the Shadow World to bring sickness and havoc amongst us. You must leave this place.'

"Bey stood up to speak for her son. 'I tell you now, my people; this is Kumsa. Look at his knee. That is the cut at his knee that he made as a child as he played with a sharp stone. There were tears in his eyes, and I cleaned his wound and held him in my arms until he slept in them. It is Kumsa I tell you. I knew his walk as he came, before my eyes knew it to even be that of a man. Please do not fear my son, it is he who has come.'

"'I am Tasa. Do you not know me people? I am the one who has grown up amongst you. This is Kumsa, my husband. I know his walk and have grown up along side him. I have been in his hut. I know his talk and his touch. No Zhun/twa can come to me and say that this is not Kumsa, my lost husband.'

"'I am Dem. I am your husband now. This is not Kumsa, this is a demon from the Shadow World who has come to bring sickness. Go from this place, thing from the dark world. You must go now.'

"'Dem, I am Tasa, your wife. How can you think that I not know my first husband? This Zhun/twa is Kumsa. Do you think that my mind and heart do not know my first husband? This is the man that I cried over for many years. Even after I had married you, I thought of him when I was in your arms. But I am your wife now, this is true, but you must believe that this is Kumsa. We do not want any trouble in this place now.'

"Dem stepped forward to grab the wrist of Tasa, bringing her around to him, 'That is not my concern. My concern is that he will bring sickness upon us. He has lived with the devils too long. He must go from here. I saw Kumsa taken by the great water to the west.

"'Go from here Kumsa,' someone shouted.

"Gau, the father of Kumsa spoke in his son's behalf. 'I am an old man now. I cannot travel far and hunt as I once could, and my eyes are not young anymore in my head, but this is my son. It is Kumsa that sits next to me now. This one I placed at my shoulders and carried around as a child. Please believe me. This man is my son whom I have cared for.'

"As the morning became the afternoon, the discussions continued. Some Zhun/twasi believed that it was Kumsa. Some did not care, and others were not sure. Some people went to the well for water and ate at their fires and scratched their heads as they discussed the concern before them. No one was for certain. But they were all afraid of the sickness that one might bring if he were at any time in the Shadow World. They discussed it until the sun reached the late afternoon. And at that time a group of men armed with bows and poison arrows and led by Kashe and Dem came to the hut of Gau and Bey.

"'Kumsa, I am Kashe. We have friends and families here. I saw the great water take you away from the land. You are dead. Bring no havoc upon us. One from the Shadow World, come from the hut of Gau and Bey. You must leave this place.'

"Kumsa stuck his head from the hut and stood to confront the men as Tasa came from the hut of Dem to stand with Kumsa.

"'Dem, I am Tasa. I am your wife now. Kumsa was my first husband. I cannot lie to you that I do not still have his heart in me. But I am yours. Do not do this thing that I think

A True Story

you will do because of the hearts we share. If you do, I shall always hate you. Let Kumsa stay. I promise to you that I will not lie down with Kumsa. It is Kumsa that is here before you. Not a spirit from the Shadow World. It is Kumsa. I know his talk and smell. Go away from Kumsa, and let him stay with his family. We will take our hut and move to another village. I give to you my word. I will not let Kumsa come between us now. Let Kumsa stay. His journey has been a long and hard one to this place.'

"'You, the one that calls himself Kumsa. I am Dem. You must go away from this place or there will be no peace here. Go away now. Our people in other villages already know of your evil spirit and will banish you on your arrival to them. You will only bring sickness and harm to the Zhun/twasi who are here and about.'

"Kumsa looked around at the people who had surround him and his family and started to walk away, and as his parents began to make their voices heard, he made them quiet with his hands. As he started away, the men and others who had gathered parted to let him leave, and he turned for one last time and hugged his mother and father, and his voice whispered in her ear and she said, 'I am old Kumsa. I cannot leave this place. My feet cannot carry me far from here, and your father's eyes are weak also. He cannot see and hunt as he once could. We are weak as children now.'

"Kumsa started off into the bush, and he turned and looked back at his people. As he walked, he leaned to the right and his arms swung behind him and he twisted and turned to avoid the bush and impressions in the earth until his figure became invisible in the land."

"Grandfather, tell use the rest of the story. Tell my friends the rest of the story."

"Listen to me little one. I have not finished. Let me catch my breath. Hand me that water.

"Well, that night things were quiet around the village. No one said much to anyone. And people stood off to the side and only looked at Gau and Bey. When the darkness came

79

to the earth, all the people went to their huts. Gau and Bey went to their hut, Tasa and Dem went to their hut, and Kashe and his wife went to their hut, as did everybody else.

"In the morning when the sun came back to the earth, Gau and Bey came from their huts as they always had, all the others came from their huts as they always had, but only Dem came from his hut alone and found that Tasa had left in the night. Tasa had followed the tracks of Kumsa, and when Dem and the others followed her tracks they met up with those of Kumsa many miles away, and there was a place in the sand that they had stood for a very long time embraced. And no one every heard from them again."

"Is that a true story Grandfather? Did that really happened."

"Yes, yes, it is a true story. It was told to me as a child, as it was told to my father and mother and their fathers and mothers."

"Where did they go?" a little boy asked.

"Dem and the others followed their tracks until they lost them. For some weeks more they searched until they found tracks again. For some time they followed them to the land of the Hereors and to the great water. When the others had given up and left Dem on his own, he followed their tracks farther then any Zhun/twa had every followed any one along the shore of the great water south to the Cape.

"From there Dem found that Kumsa knew the people, for he had been by that way many times before on the sea, and Kumsa knew the great water and how it thought and felt under its vastness.

"Dem found where Kumsa and Tasa had traded for a small boat and sailed along the coast around the Cape, north to the land of the Muslims, and it was heard that they went to the land of the Hindus, on to the land that the people made silk from worms and to the end of the earth."

A Wife Always Alone

I am a salesman by profession, and business had been good that day. The rocking of my car reminded me of the "tunnel of love" at the amusement park. As a pre-teen, my friends and I would ride—or rock—the boat as it floated silently through the tunnel. I thought of those days amongst other things as I approached North Drive along the lake.

My car broke a path down North Drive effortlessly; I could hear the wind as it whistled through the rims of my tires. It was a gray overcast day, and there had been very little snow that week. I heralded that thought as precipitation from the heavens struck my windshield as I drove uninhibited down the smoothness of the outstretched pavement.

I wanted to make one or maybe two stops before reaching home, but the rain diabolically changed slowly to slush, and then to a light powder that became heavier, more copious as I drove south. Traffic began to slow initially and climaxed to a lethargic crawl. My patience evaporated, as the winter darkness approached.

I decided to make a detour to manage my time better, but like an island this thing appeared out of the foggy snow and awaited me as I drove closer. It was a monument to

Memoirs of a Taxi Driver

mankind, a monument to civilization I saw before me that late afternoon. I remembered entering the building as a child on school outings, and now it sat off to itself, tall, supercilious, and grand.

Seeing that the unholiness I was submerged in was unrelenting, I found a parking space in the parking lot adjacent to that leviathan in front of me and sat for a moment contemplating the large number of stairs that ascended its bulk. Carefully stepping, the entrance that seemed so distant gradually revealed its awesomeness as I climbed with care and understanding toward it. Entering through the revolving doors, the warmth of the foyer greeted me with compassion as it struck my face. I stepped slowly to avoid any acknowledgement from the museum guards. Pausing for a moment, I took a wing to my right, studying specimens that were collected and displayed there. As I walked I could hear the metal plates of my shoes as they met the floor with a "tap."

Looking to my right, I saw a stairway that led down to another level. Taking those stairs brought me to a museum display case, a wooden case, topped with sparkling glass that attracted my attention with its solitude. Taking measured steps I approached, placed my fingertips on the wood trimming of the display case to avoid the glass and looked down into its configuration. I stood there for a great while studying the mummified remains and possessions that were found with it, placed painstakingly and exactly as they where discovered next to that mother of our past. I stood there looking, studying the display.

The museum display was assembled, as it would have been in the desert at burial time. There was a shallow pit dug into sand in the display. In it was placed first a grass mat held together by cords of flax: On that rested the body, with limbs flexed in the so called "embryonic posture," over it was thrown a garment of skins, that in turn was covered by a woven linen cloth. A second grass mat constituted the final protection against the desert sand, which the pit was

A Wife Always Alone

refilled with after burial. Around the body were set jars of food and drink by the museum staff, even toilet requisites were provided.

The mummy before me was very old, I wondered if that mother could have known that one day I would be standing over her, peering through sparkling glass, watching and studying her remains? Had the sun shone on her as it had shone on me and millions, and billions of people since her passing? Was she a mother? Did anyone ever love her? Did she celebrate holidays? Was there mostly hurt and pain in her life or mostly happiness? What was her name I asked myself?

That mummy, so old, so alone, made me think of my mother.

When my mother came from the South, she came from work and toil in the cotton fields. She was always working. With seven children to feed, what mother could stop working? She never had a good husband to help her. My aunt told me my mother really came to find a husband when she came to the city. There were no potential husbands down a muddy road in the backwoods of Mississippi. She was young and impatient. She did marry, and when she died my aunt told me she had found my father in an alley. I laughed at that revelation, as she stood petite before me.

My father was gone for thirty years from our lives. I would wonder sometimes what it would be like to have a father as a boy. I never told my aunt the day before my mother died she was so thin her wedding ring manumitted itself from her finger onto the bed lining. With a salty tear at my lips I kissed her hand.

A woman in pain, a wife always alone, that is what I can remember about my mother.

I studied the display just a little longer and departed observing a few more outstanding collections. I kept thinking and looking back at the display that had possessed me for so long in that secluded corner, sequestered from the other artifacts, opaque, unattractive in its existence. Only on approaching very closely would one have known that a display lay in the wooden cabinet.

A loud horn sounded; a verbal announcement was given. The museum was closing; my steps became more rapid as I reached for the egress with long strides, my metal plates under my shoes announced my advent.

The snow had deepened as I stepped out into the ferocious wind that had arrived with it. It took a large fold of my coat and flung it to my back, tossing it about before I could button it down. Dancing down the stairs, and from the stairs running across the service drive that separated the parking lot from the building, I threw myself into the confines of my car.

The traffic was more civilized; I would be home shortly.

After starting my car, I looked up at the museum and saw the cold nightlights shimmering up and down its Greek columns and the snow flickering and swirling about its vast, hard-tall walls. I knew the mummy was inside in her darkness. I wondered if she felt alone in the darkness.

I shall visit my mother before work I thought. She is not far from me.

I started my car, slowly creeping from the parking area; the snow was deeper than I had thought.

Chidi Chukwu, the Foolish

My real name is Chidi Chukwu. When I came to this country, I changed my name to Chad Covington. My real name was too difficult for the people here to say; they would use abbreviated monikers for my real name or avoided using it at all. I was born in the Congo along a river that flowed its water by my village. It is a land far away from here, where the forests are green with life, and the rain falls significantly. My father was an Ibo from the west of the continent, and my mother was Tswana from the south. I have an older brother and a younger sister. My sister is now married and my brother will soon be. We spent many of our formative years along the river. It was a rich river with an abundance of fishes, and bovine beasts came to drink from its water. When the ferry came, my family would row our boat along the side of it to sell our wares to the people on board. All that would happen while the ferry was still moving down and away from our village. Once my father could not catch the ferry to secure our vessel properly, we overturned, and all we had was lost to the river.

There were always too many people on the ferry. They almost always had to stand on top of one another, and the ferry was almost always broken down. If that ferry failed near our village, our business increased, and the income was rewarding.

When I was nine-years-old, my family moved to a small town in Nigeria away from the Congo. We had little money. Sometimes, from what I was told, we had no money. But my father did not capitulate. He did not abandon us, as some fathers have been known to do to their families. He secured a vocation with another Ibo man that owned a small business in the center of town. We went with that and survived.

My father always worked hard. My mother always worked harder, because she had to work outside our home in a full-time profession, and concomitantly doing housework after her regular job to take care of our family. I was a good student. I was always more academically inclined then my older brother and younger sister. I sometimes, all the times it seems now, would have to help them with their lessons. I was such a good student. I studied at a Jesuit school after I graduated from grammar school. My parents did not have to pay any tuition for me because I was such a good student there. One of the fathers would pay for me. I was a beautiful child. People would always want to hold me. My family has pictures to show me as a child. I was never treated unfairly there at my school, or anywhere.

Before I was graduated, I was accepted at the university in this country. They gave me a full scholarship here. I was proud; my family was proud; it was a big event for everybody. After I had come here, I did not abide by the scholarship plan. I started to socialize with the wrong people, and I forgot my purpose and direction. I started to drink, and there were plenty of girls on campus. There were women everywhere. My grades became deficient. I lost my scholarship in my second year, and my money became less for me. I disappointed a lot a people. I was ashamed, and I lost sleep over my behavior.

It was impossible for my family to sustain me. They were barely maintaining themselves back home, so, that is how I

Chidi Chukwu, the Foolish

came to drive a taxicab in this city. All types of people from all over the world drive taxis. They are from all vocations: doctors, lawyers, and accountant—you name it—the people I speak of are from all over the planet.

I usually drove late into night. I would start at six o'clock in the evening after my classes and studying had terminated. I would sometimes drive until six o'clock in the morning if I did not have classes the next day. But that is not what I am here to tell you. How should I start this story?

One summer morning, just a few hours before the sun was to return to the sky, it began to rain. It did not rain hard, but it rained very hard to the earth that morning. The rain came down in sheets. Every rambunctious sheet of rain was methodical in its decent and precise in its application of its wetness across the pavement around my yellow taxi motor vehicle. I cannot remember it raining as viciously in all my life as it did that early morning. But that was the night, the morning, it all sequentially started.

It was raining too hard for me to drive with comfort. My eyes would not do a good job at seeing through the wet water on my windshield. I curtailed my effort at driving. It was dangerous; it would have been almost fruitless to do so. I saw no people standing on the corners or perambulating the city streets to hale a cab that morning. So, I only sat in my taxi and waited for a call to come in on my computer terminal and watched from left to right in my mirrors for a human person that might approach me on the street. I never wanted anyone to approach me from behind without knowing about it beforehand. A taxi driver can never be too careful. But someone did without any of my senses warning me. It was a man with a straw hat on his head standing at the passenger side of the taxi, imploring admittance from the storm with soft knuckle taps at its window. I could see that he had been drinking but admitted him anyway. The rain was unkind to any human on the street that nighttime morning. He was not at all a kind person in his state of drunkenness, and he scolded me profusely. I only sat in my

Memoirs of a Taxi Driver

position at the steering wheel and watched him cautiously through my rearview mirror.

I inquired about his destination after his verbal vituperations had terminated, and he had no destination. I next asked if he had any currency to pay for transportation. He again verbally scolded me with words that my tympanic membranes had not heard during their existence with me. I interjected with a forefinger pointed at him and a raised voice. He produced a large supply of U.S. currency that immediately answered my question and threw some of that currency into the front seat were I reposed. I returned all that he had thrown to his area in the back seat. I told him he had given me too much currency and that we would settle the fare at his destination. I was only concerned if he had the money for the trip.

He only wanted to drive about the dark morning, but that passenger was not in a state to be driven around, and I suggested that he make his place of abode his destination. He had been drinking. I did not want the companionship of a drunken human being with me. With a few words of disagreement, he finally relented and had me drive him to his home in a suburb far away from the city center. Not far, not a long distance in the least had we driven, when that drunken man began to cry like a woman. His shoulders began to tremble and move up and down as those of the female gender. I asked him way he cried, and he started his story between his female sobs and gasped for breath.

He told me he was a brain surgeon. That night he had performed a planned surgery on a child who was hemorrhaging on one side of the brain. He volunteered in telling me that the hospital had given him the X-rays for the wrong side of the head, and he had operated on that wrong side of the head. Opening that wrong side, it was found that it was indeed the wrong side. He could not vacate that wrong side of the head before it was too late. Because of that, the young child began to hemorrhage on that wrong side of the brain he had entered to perform surgery. He had

Chidi Chukwu, the Foolish

to stop the hemorrhaging on that wrong side, vacate it, and operate on the side of the brain that was the initial concern. In that turmoil, the child died in his possession. He sobbed like a child while telling me that, and his mouth would be open with its insides visible. He had no concern about his appearance.

That doctor, I tell you now, continued to sob profusely. He wanted to die, he mentioned to me. He folded his hands and prayed. He promised allegiance to God and asked God while I was in transient with him to give him another chance at reformation. I felt pain inside my heart for that doctor, and I offered words of compassion. My strength had left me after driving so long that night, I did not make much money that night, but inside I celebrated the goodness I had by not being in his shoes.

I drove him far from the city to the country places that make up the suburbs of a large city. On our way there, a man stood by a car broken down and placed his arm out for some assistance.

On I drove until we came to his destination. It was there that he disembarked to walk to his place of residence, but not before I offered more words of encouragement. He waved to me goodbye at his door. I watched him until the hat he wore disappeared behind the apartment building door. I looked at the door he had entered and wondered how he would manage. After I had discharged that one man at his destination is how I came to the man and events that changed my life for the worst.

The rain had stopped. The sun came forward in its itinerary for the day, and I commenced my journey back to the city through the winding country roads but stopped at a donut shop not far from my last passenger's home. After I had purchased donuts and coffee, I used the venue I had arrived to that country destination to return to my city home. Some miles along the way down a small road I had arrived on, was the man that had signaled me with his arm. He carried several small and medium sized white bags, which could have been, I supposed, be from the car he had abandoned. He signaled me again but that time with significance, and I pulled over with lethargy in my body to discover his emergency.

His hands and face were appareled with moisture from the physical effort he indulged himself in while walking and carrying the packages. He was not an old man, but a man in his late fifties with a belly that stood out from lack of exercise. He spoke through the front passenger-side window I had engaged to a reclining position and told me--almost with a plea--that he needed my services. With an ample supply of blond graying hair falling in his face, he explained to me that his car had broken down on his way home and that he needed me to take him to a place in the center of the state far from the county which my city was located. He tried to persuade me by offering a large sum of money. But his ride would have been a two-hour ride. I was very tired. I had no license to pick him up where he stood, and I did not want to take him.

I explained that to him, and he told me that he would pay six times what the taxi meter would read and pay $200.00 in advance. That offer, I could not turn down and sleep at night. I did accommodate him. We drove on and he thanked me as we drove. He was a pleasant man. Listening to him, I knew him to be a fine person. He explained to me that he had medicine in his begs for his daughter, that he had to get home immediately, and that I was his salvation. We talked as we drove. I could not hear him clearly because my strength had left me, and I would for only a fraction of a second dozed off to sleep without him being suspect. Because of my paucity of strength, I would whistle and ask my passenger questions the first hour, and I am abysmally ashamed to say during the second hour, I would have to pinch my thigh with my fingernail to stay cognizant of the road in front of me. But we drove on until the corn and wheat fields became wooded and the wooded landscape became wooded with hilly and rolling forests.

Chidi Chukwu, the Foolish

We went from the main road to a smaller road that lay itself for several miles into the land. On that road it was wild, with my own sighting of a deer with her fawn and a black bear distancing itself from the road. We rode on until I did wonder when we might come to the road's end, and on my questioning him he mentioned only a short distance, and that end did come as he had said in only a very few minutes. We came to a driveway hidden by the forest trees, and we pulled into it to cover a distance of land that was impressive with its territory. That was indeed a secluded enclave. It surprised my eyes as we drove from out of the trees, and I became more alert in my senses. There was a large courtyard with beautifully manicured lawns, patterned walkways and paths. The home was built almost like a castle, with renaissance stone, limestone, and copper details. Some other cottages stood about the main domicile, and not far from that setting was a small airplane runway with a Cessna at its edge.

As we pulled up to the ingress of that castle in the forest, a large man with an exquisitely trimmed beard stood there with the uniform of a butler on his person. My passenger after leaving the taxi stood and exchanged words at the doorway with the butler. He then handed the packages to the man, and, while still holding on to them, pointed with his elbow in a direction that the butler seemed to acknowledge with a nod. My passenger disappeared into the large house as the butler walked towards his destination as he had been directed to. The passenger returned and paid me as he had promised me. He seemed to be more refreshed, more relaxed now that he was home. He smiled and I noticed rows of perfectly aligned teeth. He thanked me again. After thanking him for the business that he had given me, I prepared to leave and a sound from him stopped me. He told me he had seen that I was dozing at the steering wheel on our way to his home, and he wondered if I would stay for a few hours in his guest bedroom to regenerate my strengths. My polite response was to say no. I did say no, but he insisted, and I let him force me to agree. I was profoundly tired, and I would only have stopped along the road to sleep in the car to recover anyhow.

As he was showing me to my room in his home, there were to be antiques on the walls, floors, and ample amounts of stainless steel appliances in the kitchen that we passed. Just as we were to pass the stair casing that led to the upper level of the home, three beautiful females descended the stair casing properly refreshed and dressed for the day ahead. I was somewhat embarrassed because I was tired and needed a shower myself. I tried with all my powers not to stare at the gorgeous creatures before me, but it was a hopeless endeavor.

They were all blond females with perfectly made teeth and cologne that brought freshness to the air that surrounded them. They were of medium height with no imperfection. He introduced one of the women as his wife and the other two as his daughters. They all stood one or two steps above us during the introduction, looking down upon us. They all seemed to be the same age, and his wife revealed her maturity immediately by offering her hand to shake. It was a small feminine hand, very soft, very formal in its application. She looked at me with eyes that were very clear and rested. They were cordial to me, very lady like to me, and they did not prolong their stay after the introduction and proceeded to a dining area. I was quite impressed with them and wanted to ask my host what it was like to live in a house with such beautiful females. But I did not asked. I was very tired.

I was shown to my room, and after only a few minutes of viewing its confines I laid myself down and fell asleep immediately. Upon my awakening I did not know where I was, and after a moment I recalled how I had come to the bedroom. I had only been asleep 6 hours, and I was ready to leave but only needed to freshen up.

I set myself up to commence that responsibility when I became aware that my room was by a swimming pool. I had neglected to shut the Venetian blinds. Next, I saw the three females I had been introduced to at the swimming pool area next to my bedroom. I worried if I had been an embarrassment to myself while sleeping or to them. I clandestinely observed them, and they did not at all seem to watch me. They only talked and laughed as women do amongst themselves. I engaged the blinds to my specifications, freshened up and left from my room to retrieve my taxi.

I walked about the house until I came to the foyer and decided to return to the inner confines of the house to make enough noise to let my host know that I was departing from his hospitality. I walked towards the kitchen with the metal plates at the bottom of my shoes announcing my advent. I peeked through the door of the kitchen, and the butler without his jacket and an apron at his waist was preparing, it seemed, some repast for the family. I made myself known to him and he acknowledged me with a raised brow. He smiled and stopped me with a forefinger and said that Mr. Gur asked to be informed on my departure. He disappeared through a door laterally from my own, and in a few moments my host approached me from behind as I stood in the doorway of the kitchen.

He spoke and smiled with perfectly straight teeth and extended his hand to shake. He was friendly, grasped my hand tightly and asked if I had rested well. I told him I had rested well and that I had to be on my way back home before nightfall. He walked me to my car and thanked me again for driving him such a great distance. I thanked him for the business he had provided me, and his kind hospitality. The hospitality I told him was something that he did not have to provide.

On our advent to my car there was a large pool of automobile fluid beneath the engine compartment, and on further investigation it was discovered by me to be transmission fluid. This was devastating for me because I had really wanted to leave, for I had other responsibilities at home and a class the next day I wanted to study for.

My guest insisted on having his man call a tow truck to tow my car to a village not far from his estate and insisted that I stay with him until my vehicle was repaired. With a finger scratching my forehead, my summation was that I had no other alternative and accepted gratefully. He told me that they were about to have lunch at the pool and invited me to have lunch with them.

At the pool we did have lunch. They asked me questions about myself, questions about where I had come from, what it was like to drive a taxi, and what I was studying at the university. They were very kind, and they made me feel comfortable to be there. After those conversations the females went apart from us and began to swim in the pool. My host informed me that my car would take a few days to repair and that I was welcome to spend those days with him and his family. I was thankful for his hospitality and thought in my mind how I could repay him. He must have seen my burden and made me feel comfortable by grabbing my shoulder and shaking my hand vigorously with his other hand.

I cannot say too many times how friendly he was to me, and there seemed to be nothing wrong with that man I had picked up on a country road. He offered me a change of clothing and told me that dinner would be served at seven that evening. I went to my room, bathed and while preparing to dress fell asleep until there was a knock at the door informing me that dinner would be served in fifteen minutes. I felt splendid upon awakening. I showered that time and left for the dinning area.

The food was scrumptious, the human companionship delightful. The young women sat across from me, and Mr. Gur sat at the head of the table as a father and husband. The conversation was amicable and light. Their appetite for information about me was insatiable. They wanted to know more and more. When I spoke about myself, they listened

Chidi Chukwu, the Foolish

intently, looked directly at my mouth as I spoke, as though what I said was new and important to them and only interrupted when it was necessary. I felt quite comfortable with them, and they were all well versed in world events and well educated. After dinner we sat down comfortably in the living room of the home and talked further. I wondered about my vehicle but did not ask about its progress. What did mesmerized me was that the females seemed to covey together and laps into their own conversations apart from us and seemed very comfortable with one another. They were extremely ladylike and did not seem to have a loss for words when conversing with one another.

When it became late in the evening, I decided to retire for the night. I thanked my hosts, and I went to my room and set myself on the bed to recount the events of the day. I stood up and went to the window and peeked through the blinds and looked into the night. There was no moon out that night, and I opened the blinds and looked out into the blackness and lay back onto the bed for just a moment before removing some of my clothing to sleep. An hour might have passed before I decided to fully undress and make my rest a consummation. A few minutes had passed when there was a gentle knock at the door. Before I could respond and ready my person for admittance of a guest, the door opened and closed immediately behind someone. A woman's soft voice asked that I not turn on the light and with girlish steps she came over to the side of the bed where I lay.

She set down there beside me, told me she had seen me drive up that morning, and was sorry my car had failed me. She said it was good to have a visitor at her home, because it was rare that anyone came there. She said I was very attractive and that she was lonely without anyone really to talk to. She told me Mr. Gur was a Tartar and rarely allowed her to leave to go anyplace outside of the estate. She started to cry and said that it was a horrible life where she was. I told her that could not be the case because he was amicable

95

and kind. Not only was he that, I supposed to her, but she and the other women seemed to love him and were very relaxed around him. She told me that it was only a charade and that he was a mean and insidious villain.

We had talked only a few more minutes when she leaned over and kissed my cheek softly, then warmly touch my lips with hers. She was warm and soft and caused me to hunger for another kiss. I did solicit her for another kiss. She acquiesced and held her lips to mine. I touched her excitedly. She was warm and moist as a woman would be in that place, and I made love to her that night. I fell into a deep sleep, and, when the sun came, she was not with me. I looked around to make sure I had not been dreaming, and I had not been dreaming. The remnants of the night before were with me. I rose and showered and prepared myself for breakfast. There was a knock at the door informing me that breakfast would be served at eight o'clock. I finished promptly and left for the dinning area.

At breakfast the conversation was cordial as we sat around the table in our previous arrangement. The women were polite and attentive, but as I said before, they sat close to one another and seemed to have a comfort amongst themselves that was inseparable. They lapsed into conversation amongst themselves as if there were no men in the room to be dealt with. They were very comfortable with one another, and when they laughed or giggled, their mouths would leave no morsel of food to fall or to be seen from their mouths. Their hair seemed to have been prepared for hours in front of a mirror, and it did not move from its place atop their heads to become discombobulated as they socialized. They were all fresh, clean, and well groomed—as you might find the pictures of women in a woman's fashion magazine.

In our conversations I tried to give a signal to the woman I had made love to that night, but there was no signal from any of the women I could summarize. At the pool that day we sat and talked, I tried with all my senses to see, give a

Chidi Chukwu, the Foolish

signal, or hint to one of the women that held me in the night, but no hint or coquetry was forthcoming. I felt somewhat foolish in my effort to communicate with no response from my confidant. At dinner I gave up my efforts and retired early to my bedroom. For the second night the moon did not visit this forest enclave, and after reading--or scanning you might say--some books that were provided for me, I relaxed and turned off the lights for the night. Not more than five minutes after I had accomplished that is when there was a soft knock at the door, and my visitor from the night before entered and whispered to me not to turn the lights on because someone might see us.

She was very light with her feet and was by my bedside within a thought. I asked her why she had not signaled me that afternoon and evening. She told me that the others were watching her and that we had to be careful. I asked her which one of the women she was, and she would not answer me and only said that what appeared to be around her home was not what it appeared. She kissed me and told me that she could not wait until the night came because she wanted to be with me. She was so lonely she told me. She said she had been secretly watching me all day and every moment at the pool she was hungry to be with me. She kissed me. I kissed her and she was good in my arms. I held her. I kissed her. I was violent with her.

We both slept. When the morning came, she had gone from me. I was angry with myself for not insisting that she tell me which woman she was amongst the three and falling asleep before I could get her to confess to me. I showered and dressed. When there was a knock on the door for breakfast, I was there to open it to acknowledge to the butler I would be on time. He had a covered tray in one hand with what appeared to be a hot meal and walked away. Again, at the table there was not the slightest nuance from any of the women to indicate that I had been with one of them. Our conversations were those of friends and family. At the pool I swam with swimming trunks loaned to me by my host,

Memoirs of a Taxi Driver

and there was nothing in the continence of the women to incriminate any of them.

That night after dinner, my host took me on a tour of his estate and some of the forestland that surrounded it. As we walked, he informed me that my car would be ready in the morning and that I could be on my way. He reiterated his thanks to me and told me he felt a little guilty for bringing me so far from home and that he would take care of the bill for the repairs made on my car. I confessed to him I was horribly embarrassed that he had seen me dozing off on our way to his home. As we walked he told me that being a husband and a father had taught him to not quite speak out unless it became completely and irretrievably impossible not to. He said he knew I was tired and had planned to have me stop for some coffee. But I seemed to be doing quite well in my driving, and it did not seem impossible for me to continue.

I felt this man had discovered a foible in me. He knew I was sleeping while driving him. And I wondered if he knew I was only telling him and his family only about the successes and good things in my life? I wondered if he could see in my eyes the scholarship I had desecrated and the drinking and women that had torn me down? Did he know about my unfaithfulness with one of his family members but was too kind to mention it to me? I felt some shame and had no alternative but to offer that he take the check back he had given me and give me a lesser amount as a ballast for my unveracious ways. He had fed me, provided me a place to sleep, shower—it was too much I felt. But he refused me, and we walked down and about his property and talked.

I questioned him about his property as an invited guest would, and obliquely asked him if only his two daughters and wife lived on it. Without hesitation he acknowledged that it was the case, and we continued until our time was up and directed our itinerary toward the house, enjoying the evening forest sounds.

Chidi Chukwu, the Foolish

When I got back to my room, my cloths were freshly cleaned, pressed, and hung in view so that I could see them. I reminded myself mentally that I would put my clothing on and not the ones that were loaned to me during my stay the next morning. There was no television in my room so I read hoping that she would return on my last night there. I read until my eyes became heavy and they closed without my knowing, and I was asleep. I awoke in the middle of the night to find the light still on in my bedroom, and I turned it off and lay on my left side and watched for the motion of the dark water of the pool that lay outside my patio window. I could not see the water. Again the moon did not come out that night, and I wondered if she had come that night to my bedroom door and knocked, but because I did not answer she left.

I was disappointed and searched for her sound with my ears. I rose to walk to the window to see if I focused my eyes hard enough that maybe I could see the pool's water. There was gentle knock at the door. I knew it was she at the door. When I answered gently, the door open and she came in. She walked into the room and walked over to the sound of my voice and held me. She told me she had been waiting for me to turn the lights out so that she could come to me. I asked her why she had to do that, and she said because they were watching her and someone might have seen. I felt she had not been direct with me about the truth. I took her by the shoulders and lead her to the bed and asked why she did not signal me earlier that day. I told her that my car would be ready, and that I would be leaving in the morning. I wanted to know how we could continue our relationship if I did not know who she was. I wanted to know how I could contact her in the future.

She began to cry and told me not to leave. She was lonely she said, and they were secretly mean to her she said. I asked her if she wanted to come with me, and she told me that she could not. They would not let her; they were overpowering and mean. She lay back onto the bed on her left side and pulled me down beside her and stroked the side of my face. She kissed me kindly as a friend would. I kissed her. I felt something inside for her, and we made love that night. I bit her many times, and her voice made sounds that were feminine. I would not stop with her. I became one with her, and we lay and talked afterwards, and we then started again with one another until she and I did not have any strength inside of us.

When I awoke, saw that she had gone away and the light was in the sky, I jumped from the bed with sleep still over me and cursed, went to the patio window to see if she had left from that way, and quickly went to the door to look out of it into the hall. There was nothing to be seen of her, and I went into the shower to prepare myself. When there was a knock at the door, I answered with my voice and acknowledged that I would be ready for the breakfast that awaited me. There was the sound of a tray and glass being dropped by the butler outside my door, and I opened it to assist him if I could. He told me that he could manage the cleanup without any assistance, and I went back into my room to make my final preparations.

During breakfast there was no nuance from the woman that one of them had intimate encounters with me. This angered me. They were just as cordial and presentable. They advertised their sorrow that I would have to be leaving them and wished me well. They departed the table early to some unknown venue of the house, but on my arrival at the door to exit the house, they came to where I stood as a group, without prejudice and convincingly said goodbye to me. At that time I was convinced that a signal would be sent to me, but there was no signal and my host walked me out of the door down a winding path to my car that had been prepared for me. The women stood at the door, very beautiful women they were, and waved at a distance.

At this time I saw the butler leave out of the door walking around them with a tray of food covered as food would be in transient and walked over to a coach house that sat

Chidi Chukwu, the Foolish

directly across from my room on the other side of the pool which I had not noticed during my stay. On the upper floor there were curtails as if a home had been made out of it. He opened its door and went inside and within a few minutes exited without the tray.

My keys were in the ignition, and I was relaxed with my host in our final fair wells. He asked me if I knew the way back to the main highway and handed me a map he held in his hand. He shook my hand and told me it had been an honor to have me as a guest in his home. I took the door to my taxi and opened it, preparing to sit down in its confines when I stopped my decent and turned to my host and mentioned that it seemed impossible that such a large beautiful house could be for so few people. I asked him again if it was only his wife, two daughters, and himself in such a large place, and his countenance changed and his eyes looked down, moving from right to left rapidly, not in shame, but as if he were thinking, searching for some answer, some information stored away in his mind.

"Yes, yes, I do have another daughter" he said slowly.

The medicine he had with him that morning was for her he explained. He told me that she was sick. He told me that this one daughter would not listen to him as a daughter should listen to her father. She was not ladylike, and now she was sick. He did not lose his continence but spoke as a father who knew failure as a parent. I asked him if he loved her, and he confessed his love for her. I set down in my car and started the engine to hear its sounds and placed it in gear. I turned the engine off and asked him if she would recover soon and he said with a heavy voice:

"No, no, no, ... she has AIDS."

Maria

One summer evening, over there at the store across the river, is where I met the woman with whom I first fell in love. If you look closely, you will be able to see the fire hydrant I parked my car by that evening. I was going to visit my family, and I would normally have taken public transportation--that was what I was going to do--but I remembered that I would not have to do that because I could rent a taxi, work a few hours and use the taxi to drive to my parents' house and leave as late as I wanted. I secured the vehicle in the afternoon, and while driving by a pharmacy, I stopped in to purchase something that is not important in my mind now, but was very important in my mind then. I walked up to the counter and a young girl stood before me. She was maybe fifteen or sixteen-years-old. She was so lovely; she was so charming as she looked around waiting for some service from the clerk not yet there before her. With each toss and turn of her head the store's lights would shimmy down each strand of her hair.

That night at my apartment, Maria was a wild woman. She ripped and tore at my shirt, uncontrolled, unleashed, like some feral and savage beastress, every concomitant of her femininity gone from her. She was shameless, so bold,

102

Maria

and unladylike. My breath went away from me. I could only lie there afterwards to regain my strength.

Standing behind that Maria in the pharmacy, I had no idea she was actually a twenty-one-year old woman with a young daughter. At first the relationship we had was smooth and unproblematic. I could not wait to get home, and we made love continually. Even at night we would wake up and make love. I would call her, she would call me, and we would talk for hours. I would sometimes ask her why a woman so beautiful, so lovely, was so available. She eventually moved in with me, and she brought her six-year-old daughter along. I was so proud of them. They were so wonderful to me. The child was so glorious, was so beautiful; she looked like she had been hand painted by God. Even today, I cannot remember a child being so lovely, so well behaved. I could not believe the prize that God had sent me, until things began to change for the worst.

It all started when I had to leave for class or maybe to work. Maria wanted to know where I was all the time. She would set times that I was to call her, and if I did not call her, there would be no peace when I returned home that night. At first that was no problem; I was even flattered that such a lovely female would be possessive of me. After all, she was gorgeous. I had never had a woman so beautiful in my life. She was tall, with a girlish physique that was beautifully made. Physically she was perfect, with slightly bowed legs, perfectly sculptured face, and perfectly made calves. When she walked, her hips would cause the bottom of her skirt to wince from side-to-side in the back, revealing beautifully crafted calves--and thighs if the wind was rambunctious. She looked much younger than her age, and people would stand back and look at her at a distance. Men and women would compliment me on having such a lovely woman and child with me. Anything she wore she made it look perfectly crafted. A used ten-dollar dress would look perfectly fine on her. But, if I did not call her, she would drive down to the university and wait for me. She knew

103

what class I was in when she came, and she would embarrass me with her screaming.

She demanded that she select my wardrobe. She said anything I bought made me look like a tramp. If she was angry with me, she would take it out on the child. She would hit the child if she did not read or pronounce a word correctly from her homework, and several times I had to pull her off the child. I dreaded going home after driving the taxi, and our sex life diminished. When I saw her coming, she was ugly to me. I wanted to get rid of her, but deep down inside I loved her, and I loved the girl. I knew she would also take the girl away.

One day she told me that she was pregnant. I asked her what she was going to do, and she said that she was going to keep the child. I told her that we could not afford another child, and she said that she was going to keep the child because she wanted her daughter to have a playmate. I told her if she would abort the child I would marry her the following year. I was to graduate that year, and I had a job waiting for me. She refused to abort the child, and anytime I mentioned it she would retaliate with verbal and physical abuse.

One afternoon I was standing and talking to a neighbor in the lobby when Maria came down to go to the commissary in the adjoining building to purchase something. She came up to me with the door keys balled up in her fist and pounded the jagged edges of the keys into my shoulder and repeated rapidly with each strike over and over again in front of the woman, "Haven't I told you not to be standing down here talking to women, haven't I told you not to be standing down here talking to women...." I was awfully embarrassed, and the woman just walked away stunned. I was in a depressed mode all the time because of Maria.

On the day of my graduation ceremony, I decided that I was doing something wrong in the relationship and asked Maria demurely if I could talk to her after the graduation. At the graduation I was afraid to introduce her to my

Maria

classmates because of her behavior. While at the ceremony, as usual, I was often asked where I had found such a beautiful female, but I saw no beauty in that woman, I only wanted her out of my life, and I searched in my mind everyday and night how I could do such a thing. While thanking one of my professors for her expert help, Maria blurted out to her that I did not deserve to graduate, and she could not see how I did it. I was deflated inside, and I could feel my public aplomb on my face leave me in front of my professor. Maria would find ways to mortify me in public, and I had no knowledge why she performed in such a manner. She did a splendid job at the end of the graduation ceremony by screaming at me as we were about to enter our car and driving off with part of my gown fastened in the door, tearing a section completely off from me. I was totally embarrassed and looked like a fool I suppose.

I took the bus home—I was too embarrassed to have anyone after the ceremony drive me home. I felt everyone had seen. Even today I think about that intricate moment on a day that was so important to me. When I got home I did everything in my power not to strangle her. At that time I could have thrown her to the carpeting and trodden her to death with my feet.

She apologized for her behavior, but she had apologized many times before, and she would only reiterate the same fowl behavior again, again, and again. That evening after Una was asleep, she asked me what matter it was that I wanted to talk to her about. I told her that our relationship was in turmoil and that we needed counseling. She told me we did not need counseling, but I only needed counseling.

I wanted to save the relationship, but I did not have the knowledge to save a relationship with someone who needed professional therapy.

It got to the point that I had to ask permission to ask a particular question. Before I left out I had to ask if the kitchen met her specification and if a particular shirt was okay to wear. If I were going to be late getting home I would have to let her know a day ahead of time. And it got to the point that I had to go to a certain venue in our apartment to sit quietly in order to avoid her wrath. If the girl or I would move, she would complain that we were disturbing some venue of the apartment or another or causing some other damnation.

I had a job at a marketing firm waiting for me after graduation but still drove the taxi on Sundays for extra money. One day at work I got a call from Maria from the hospital, and she told me she had miscarried the baby. It was a boy she told me, and I was sad about it but happy that she would not have a child to hold over my head. When I arrived home that night, I put my arms around her and kissed her. Regardless of all her faults, Maria was good sometimes. But her temperament changed like the weather.

I was still trying to find a way to get rid of her. My life was miserable, and nothing I did was right in her eyes. I remember we were going to make love one night--that was before she was pregnant--she was complaining as I was leaning over to embrace her, I had no excitement for her.

Another time I did not want to get in the bed with her, and I was trying to wait until she went to sleep to avoid her. She would always insist that I get in the bed, and I would. She wanted me to get on top of her, and while I was getting on top of her, she was still complaining about some matter that happened earlier in the day that the child or I had done improperly. I rolled over and told her I could not take it. She never stopped complaining, and she took over every aspect of my life. She opened my mail, took all the telephone calls, made all the decisions, and I found myself asking her permission to go outside to buy a newspaper.

The last straw came when she told me she was going to buy a pistol for the house. There had been some burglaries in the building, and she said that she was afraid. I reminded her the burglaries had happened during the day and that we had a security guard during the night for protection. She refused to listen to me and went out and bought a pistol anyhow.

Maria had perfect teeth. She had never worn braces; they just grew down straight in her mouth. They were flinty white, and when she got angry they would knead together to make the muscles around the bone in her jaw move. One night while we were watching television, she took the pistol out of the buffet and started to load and unload the bullets in the pistol and said, "If I see you with another woman, man I'm going to shoot you." I had done nothing wrong, and her teeth were together with the muscles around the bone in her jaw moving. At that moment I made up my mind to leave her, and that week I secretly moved out of my own apartment to my parents' house to get away from her.

While she was at work one morning, I left my job, went home, picked up a few personal items, and moved them over to my parents' house without telling her about it. When she called my parents' house I told her that she needed therapy, and I could not be around a woman who threatened a man with a gun. She told me I would never see Una again, and I told her she was an "evil woman" and I did not hate her but felt sorry for her.

I then started to date a woman who was a few years older than I was. I met her one Sunday while driving the taxi. She was going to a seminar that would teach her how to start a business in her home. She was attractive. She was the type of woman you would never be embarrassed to walk down the street with. But she was not working, was not very bright, and had a boy and girl both under ten years old. She was attractive, but that is all she had that was worth anything. Whenever I took her to an event and asked her for an opinion, she had no opinion. Whenever we went out to dinner and we looked at the menu, I would ask her what she thought would be worth ordering; she had no thoughts about what to order. That woman was a complete dunce. Whenever we were out together, it was as if I was alone. What I liked about her though, was that she was not a mean woman, and she did everything I told her to do. She was like a cow. She just stood there and did nothing unless she was instructed to do something.

I will say this about that woman; she was not an easy woman. After I took her out on a date the first night, she did not let me make love to her. All of my verbal skills did not circumvent that woman's resolve. She fought me tooth-and-nail. Hand-to-hand-combat, that is how she fought with me. I was so tired and exhausted I gave up. She was a tall and husky woman. She was not the type of woman you could pick up in your arms and run down the street with in an emergency.

She had sixteen brothers and sisters and did not know who her father was. I told her she should ask her mother who he was, but she never got around to it, no matter how much I insisted.

That woman would never work a job. She refused to go out and get a job. I showed her all types of business proposals, job opportunities, but she never took advantage of any of my recommendations. She asked me to lend her seventy dollars one day. I told her if she did not get out and find a job she would be sorry. I refused to give her any money or lend her any money. That woman was totally lazy and waited every month for a check from the state public assistance agency. I asked her why she would not get a job; she told me that the government owed African-Americans financial support because of the slavery they put us through.

While I was seeing that woman, I was seeing Maria also. I loved Maria, I loved Una, and I was actually legally responsible for that apartment because the lease was signed by me. I did not keep any of my personal items at the apartment and only went there to make love to Maria and to see Una.

Maria would attempt to placate me. She tried to entice me to move back in with her. I was tempted, but there were some things inside of her that made me know that she needed therapy. I remember once, I caught her talking to

Maria

herself. After talking to herself, she would answer herself. That worried me a little. I was concerned about her. I mentioned therapy to her as often as I could, and she began to anticipate my mentioning it by saying, "You want to go down that road again and say I need therapy, don't you? Say it now! Go ahead, say it!"

One day, while sitting in the car on our way back from a movie, I could take no more. I went back up stairs with her following me, took the few things I did have there and left her for good. Because she had the gun and could go crazy at any moment, I wrote her a letter and told her I would like her to vacate the apartment as soon as possible, and if she did not I would have her thrown out—of course I did not mean it.

She got anger at me when she got the letter and called my parents' house and cursed me in English and lapsed into Spanish, as she would whenever she got uncontrollably angry and threw the receiver down on the floor. Una picked up the telephone and in her small voice asked, "Are you coming back to live with us?" I told her, "Well, Mama is angry. She might hit me, but I love you." I talked with her a few minutes longer and hung up the telephone. At that point, I was still secretly trying to keep the relationship going for the girl also, but it was impossible.

By accident I saw her on the apartment grounds after she had moved all of her personal belongings from the apartment. She was walking down a pathway with a man I had never seen before. I walked past them; she looked around to see if I was looking at them; she put her arms around him and hugged him. It hurt me inside, but I fought it. I never saw her again until one year later walking down a busy street, she smiled at me with a sneering grind, her flinty white teeth browner for some reason, and I asked her while passing, "How's the family?" There was no response from her. I wished she had stopped—I was dying to talk to her. After that I never saw her again. It took me a long, long time to get over losing Una. The child was so wonderful. I suffered without her a long time.

People deny a lot of things to themselves. I cannot deny that I think about my life now. I think about how I could have made my life better. I think about the relationships I have had with lovers and people in general. Sometimes I have sat at home for five and six hours, without moving, thinking about how my life could have been better. I have thought sometimes that I could have made a difference with Maria. Maria might have had some kind of syndrome. After all, she did lose the baby. It could have been some sort of post pardon disease. I do believe that it was my behavior that caused our relationship's demise. If I had more knowledge at that time, I could have made a difference in our relationship.

One day, after about ten years, I looked in the telephone book under Maria's last name. I found two names that matched her first and last names. I did not called them, but I looked at them for a long time. I knew where she worked after we ended our relationship. I was going to wait outside in my taxi one day to see if she came out, but I forgot to do it. I might have gotten busy. I forget now why I did not wait outside her job. I really think that I did not want to see her, because I might still have had feelings for her. I did not want those feelings coming back into my heart.

Now that I have these gray hairs on my head, I do not think Maria had a mental concern, I know Maria had a mental concern, and I was young and did not know what to do about it.

You must understand that I was not; I am not obsessed with Maria. That is not the only woman whom I have ever been in love with. But she was the first--I can still smell her freshness and taste the goodness of her at my lips. It is just obvious to me that some mistakes were made by me in the relationship that should not have been made.

One night, while driving a taxi, I pulled into a parking garage entrance to turn around for a passenger. I thought I

Maria

saw Maria walking into the door of a convenience store dressed up in a very flashy outfit. It looked like the ones prostitutes wear. She had a long wig on. She looked pretty good. After I dropped that passenger off I went back to that store, but there was no Maria around that area. I drove around slowly looking for her, and I did not find her. I saw Maria's sister once at night. She did not see me as she looked away into a store window. I hid my face from her and kept driving. The woman had not aged a day. But, secretly, I would look for Maria. I would wonder where she could be and how she was in the world. I hid that desire to know from myself. In the city center I hoped that I would come upon her, and I would speak to her handsomely as I did as a young man.

Once I caught a police officer having sex with a prostitute. I was parked in the city park near the lake on a street between cars. It was impossible to see me, because I was lying down on my right side in the front seat taking a short nape before I resumed my driving. I had been sleeping for about an hour and was refreshed enough to start my shift again. I rose up in front of the steering wheel. I saw a police sergeant parked about ten feet in front of me. On the right rear side of his squad car he had a prostitute standing outside the squad car, bent over, with her upper torso inside the squad car with her panties down around her thighs. The sergeant was humping her from behind.

I sat there amazed at first and smiling in the end without them knowing I was there. I did not move, but when he finished his work he saw me, repaired himself, said a few words to the woman, had her sit down in the squad car, walked around to his door, and drove away embarrassed I surmise. I tell that story every time I can remember to tell it. What bothered me that night, is that prostitute looked just like Maria. She looked just like Maria. I put it out of my mind because it had been fifteen years since I had seen her. My mind was playing games with me.

Memoirs of a Taxi Driver

It had been over forty years since I had last seen Maria. I will be sixty-two-years old next month, and I do not drive as many days as I did when I was in my twenties. I do drive although. It is a part of me; after a week of not driving I become bored.

One late winter afternoon I wished I had not been driving and stayed at home bored. I was coming out of a small grocery store in a neighborhood were the sun never shines and the rain always falls and set down inside of my taxi. That neighborhood was a horrible place to be in for almost anyone. The people are always in a bad way there. It was cold outside, and I was unfortunate enough to lease a taxi without a functioning heater. I had to stay bundled up against the cold of the outside when I stepped outside the taxi, and I had to stay bundled up against the cold with a scarf and earmuffs on the inside of the taxi when I stepped back into the taxi from the outside.

As I was walking to my taxi, I saw an old woman coming down the street with a gentleman in a slow walk. She was in an intense conversation with him, but that circumstance did not leave an impression in my mind. I wanted to get started before the shift was over and make my income for that night. I remember I sat there on that corner eating a small cake I had bought and trying to decide which direction I should drive to increase my chances of picking up a taxi customer.

I finished the small cake and prepared to depart. Just as I had started to drive away, the old woman bundled up with hat and scarf all about her face, signaled me. I halted my movement forward and waited for her to approach me. She reached for the taxi door directly behind me, and I signaled with my voice and hand for her to enter the taxi in the rear at the door that was not directly behind me.

She set down on that side and sighed a relief from the cold that I understood. I hoped that she would not notice that my heater was not working and ask me to turn it on, so, I interjected before she could speak, and asked her how I

Maria

could help her. She told me she had to make two stops: one to pick up her daughter, and the other stop would be her home.

At her behest I started on our way, and she did ask for the heater just as I had hoped she would not. I told her the condition of the heater and she cursed a word in my direction and looked away through the passenger window and became silent. As I was driving, through my scarf around my face, I could smell that this woman had not had a bath for a few weeks. I looked at her more closely through my rearview mirror and saw by her apparel that she was a homeless lady, and I realized the man she had been discoursing with, to be a man she had been soliciting for some money. I immediately told her that her destination was a long one and asked if she had the money for the ride. She cursed a word at me, and pulled green money from one of her pockets, and showed it to me with a holey cloth glove covering her dirty fingers.

I told her to count it to make sure it was all there, because I did not want a fare that did not generate a profit for me that night, and she counted the money and reported to me that it was sufficient for the trip. She was a tattered old woman. I could not see her mouth, but her eyes were creased with crow's-feet, and they were dirty all around. As we drove she mumbled words to herself and was lost in her thoughts as the city passed in front of her.

She laughed out loud and cursed to herself, pointed accusingly at some person that was not outside the window but only in her thoughts I supposed. Her wool scarf would fall away from her face when she laughed and that made her face and eyes appear to be crooked. I could not wait until I could discharge that woman from me and contemplated how I would handle her if she did not give me all the funds that would be owed me. You have to understand that I am not a young man anymore, and I cannot wrestle with insane people as I once could.

Memoirs of a Taxi Driver

As we went on, she laughed one long time, and her lips came untangled from her scarf and dark empty spaces surrounded two remaining brown teeth in her mouth and she immediately covered her lips from the cold and continued her conversations with people unseen by me. I wanted to make sure that she was not too crazy to have given me the wrong directions and asked her if we were still headed in the right direction. She answered me as a sane person would, and told me to continue, and that we were not far away. "Continue, continue, you're doing fine." With her sane answer to me I became more comfortable and drove on, content inside that she would not be a problem.

We drove on, and when we neared her destination she came out of her craziness and asked me to start slowing down. I did that at her request, and she looked out the window as one person would for an address or one looking for another person. She demanded a stop. I did stop; she looked around wildly for something that was not there but was supposed to have been there at that moment. When she was not satisfied, she told me to drive down just a little, and there on a fire hydrant sat a woman maybe in her middle forties, beautiful, but visibly, recognizably weathered from neglect and illegal substance abuse.

The younger woman stood up, seeing the taxi before the crooked faced woman saw the younger woman at the hydrant. The younger woman complained as she walked over to the older woman in the taxi.

When that younger woman brought herself inside the taxi, she complained loudly about the cold and the time she had spent at the hydrant. Then there was muffled talk between them, a counting of money, and I was told where to go. I was asked to go to a place that illegal drug substances were sold, and I halted the taxi and told both of them I would have to have money in my pocket for the entire trip before I took them to that drug place. They indicated that it was no concern and paid me, which was not enough. I asked for more, and they both complained. I told them I would not

Maria

take them if I did not receive enough money from them, and the young woman leaned forwards and offered to perform an oral sexual act on me for the balance.

I told them both that they would have to leave if they did not pay, and there was a muffled conversation between them, a counting of money between them, and they handed the money to me in my hand. With that all settled amongst us, I proceeded to their destination, with the women having a normal conversation, sprinkled with light argument and curses. Both women seemed to be on edge and asked me to hurry, and I told them if I was to be stopped for speeding we may never get there. They settled down with that knowledge, and we reached their destination, which was a dark place, a sick place, with those kinds of people with long faces, immoral thoughts, and wanton eyes, looking about that place for some kind of elusive salvation.

The older woman stopped me and pointed the younger woman in the direction of a doorway with a man standing in it, a doorway that looked not like a doorway, but was a hole in a wall to eyes that are not use to living conditions such as those.

The younger woman stepped lightly from the car as if her fruition had finally come to her and went over to the man holding her head high, words where exchanged, and a motion by the man to come inside happened; a short time passed, and the woman came from the hole that was a door to the taxi door with a rapid girlish step. I was given an order to take them to a place that existed for those who had given themselves up from the world, a homeless place, a lost place, a place for sick people steeped in illegal drugs and drink under a dark street with lights low and dim to hide the badges of failure and illness.

As we drove on, the women were happy amongst themselves, and there was no discontentment in words between them, when I heard the older woman say alertly to the younger woman in their laughter, "Una, be careful. Don't drop them." And we drove on to a building, a

115

building that has its lower facade under a street. A building where mattresses lie outside of its lower front and people lie around together on those mattresses, or in the case of the very mentally sick, alone, far away in deep conversation with themselves.

The young woman had dropped one of her purchases onto the floor and could not retrieve it in the shallow light. The older woman became enraged and beat the younger woman at the shoulder with her fist and repeated rhythmically, "Haven't I told you to be more careful, haven't I told you to be more careful, haven't I told you to be more careful." And when this was done, my mind came to me. I knew these people I felt. I stopped that woman and her protest with a flashlight I held in my hand, which I kept in my brief case for such emergencies, and directed them to step from the taxi, and as they did, I looked at them; I looked through them to make sure that my mind would not be wrong. I took a moment to look away from them, and I looked at the floor and finally lifting the seat from its sitting position to look into its crevices for what was lost. I knew what possession the beating was over. I found it with my eyes, pointed to it with a finger, and when the old woman leaned forewords to retrieve that thing, I look at her face, through her covered face, and I knew I could not be wrong. They did not thank me and turned to meet their companions that awaited them under the veil of wincing darkness, which was broken in some places by electric street lamps sparsely placed above them.

After they had gone only a few feet from me, I broke their stride and the cold silence that place had around it, "Maria! Maria!" I exclaimed. The woman stopped, turned to me with her crooked face, and her crooked eyes and asked with cadence through her scarf, "How did you know my name?"

The Fish Hunter

In the North it is very cold much of the year. When it is warmer in the North, before the winter cold leaves its apparel about the land, the North prepares itself in a myriad of ways for the winter to come: the days become less in light, burrows are dug, birds fly to where the genial warmth meets the north cold, and it has been known, many a time, for a woman to come for the man she once spurned.

In the distance above the forest and across a lake lethargic with cold, there is a movement in the cold sky. A team of dogs harnessed and lying outside the forest cabin has not noticed the novelty of the distant movement against the horizon from that of only moments earlier. It is some living thing moving across the north sky that knows its way across the land. On this floating organism comes unperturbed by the cold wind. With each passing moment it becomes obvious that it has wings that beat like that of an itinerant fish hunter. Its great wings move up and down with poetic understanding, without significant effort, through the ice-air and above the green-pine land below it.

This eagle, with its bald head ornately adorned with white crown-feathers, does not look for the fish to relieve its hunger but moves south to beat the winter cold before it

Memoirs of a Taxi Driver

lays its heavy hand upon the land with a full force. On with methodical grace the bird flies, its body a weight, a ballast between it great powerful wings, shortening its distance to the dogs and cabin with each motion of its great wings. The snow dogs are still not cognizant of the bird-king as it comes out of the clouds. It has flown along the peninsula, down along the coast water, not leaving the shore of the sea far behind to make its way down along the land to Juneau and down to the outside were the weather is propitiatory, where the winter will leave the lake waters free from the ice that is well known in the North.

Its great wings having flown so far, causes it to look for a place to rest for a time that is not too long but long enough for it to procreate its strengths and, hopefully without much effort, a morsel of food, for at this time its hunger is not profound enough to have it stop its journey for any other purpose besides rest.

Down it comes through the clouds, the air heavy with the moisture that will become the snow in a forest night. Closer it comes to the earth until it sees its sanctuary near the lake it had crossed years before on its journey to the south. Here is where it decides to make its adjournment. Its wings assail the wind, bringing itself closer to make a final commitment to the earth. Down, down, down ever so softly, so quietly, it makes its descent, the wind causing the feathers at it crown to frill as its talons come forth to meet the earth once more.

With ears that perk to attention, Whitefish is the first to observe the great bird. They regress to their previous reclining position after she notices it to be a fish hunter, one of thousands she has seen in the past. The bird becomes a momentary occlusion to her main concerns. This arrival does not disturb a hair on the deep wooly coats of the other dogs. They only continue with their slumber after their long trek across the new snow to the forest cabin.

Whitefish is her master's lead dog. Her blood is the blood of a long pedigree of dogs from the North that live to run through the winter snow and over the ice-rivers that make

The Fish Hunter

the North a land men of a special breed call home. Her only concern is her master in the cabin and the food that awaits her on the completion of her mission. She only wishes to be on her way back through the snow to home and food. It will soon be mealtime her stomach tells her.

The fish hunter finds a fallen spruce to land upon, dead for some fifty years. This is where the fish hunter places its talons and this is where it causes little notice to come from the dogs harnessed to the sleigh. It surveys the area about it and decides to alter its vantage point on a dead spruce still standing. With one sweep of its wings it is there, high above to look down on the cabin and the dogs that recline themselves in the fresh powdery snow.

It is early afternoon. The fish hunter and Whitefish direct their gaze to the cabin when human voices and other sounds radiate from its confines to the outside cold. In a corner of the cabin at a table that has a century of dust sits a young woman, swaddled in a large fur coat, one who is not accustomed to the cold of the North, and she watches the man at the small stove as he tries to bring a fire to life to warm the cabin for her. He works without gloves to do so, and she tries to understand how his fingers can work in such cold, in such an unforbiddening environment. He turns to her.

"I think that should do it."

"I hope so, Tall One of the desert. It is good to see you Tall One."

"It is good to see you Little Fox of the desert. Your beauty is still large and good to look upon even here in this land of ice and snow. My eyes cannot understand seeing you here—after they have only known you in the desert. I sometimes cannot understand how my feet came to this place; but I am here in this place. I have thought of you many times in this place. I was surprised when the Pakistani radioed me about your arrival here. You have surprised me."

"The Pakistani, what is his name? He is very pleasant."

119

Memoirs of a Taxi Driver

"His name is Syamalan. I call him Sam. We work together. You know about that, do you not?

"I know, I know about that."

The woman looks down into her hands to gather her thoughts.

"It took me many years to find you. I had fear in me that you would not see me. But I had to try. I had been looking for so long. I am so sorry in my heart because of what happen to our marriage. My beautiful husband I have failed you. I was only thirteen. I did not know anything about marriage and the world, or even what I would do with myself. I was only a child Tashelo. I have come here to take you back with me to the desert, our home. I know how good things were between us now. I never knew your skin was young and smooth. Not all men have skin so beautiful at their faces. I did not know you were so handsome. You were a good hunter Tashelo, and I could not be satisfied with that inside of me then Tashelo. You were a good provider, and I was deep inside your heart. I see that now."

The man listens profoundly and bites at his mustache while placing his hands in his pants pockets under his parka, feeling flocculent bits of fabric for the first time while walking towards the window to look far off into the forest. His optic fibers see the eagle perched in the rotting pine and the dogs, but they looked pass them all, his mind is absorbing the meaning of the words the young woman had spoken. He spreads his legs, hunches his shoulders, and looks down to the floor before speaking. It is a dirty floor. He thinks about how dirty it is, and he moves the dust around with his boot and wonders how he can think of a dirty floor after his wife has come from so far away. She is so beautiful to him. She removes her fur hat so that he can see her tightly napped hair. She has a small girlish head with a long thin neck—just as a teenage girl might have. She has a petite frame, and she has her left leg crossed over her right with snow still not melted from her fur boots. She appears to be nervous. She rings her hands as if she is applying an ointment of some kind to protect them from the winter cold. But this also might be because her hands are chilled.

"Thank you for speaking those words. They are nice to hear. I tried to be important to you. I wanted to prove to you that I would never fail at my work for you. It was not easy to leave the desert to travel across the earth for me. I wanted to wait for you. I did wait for you secretly. But I finally went north with a Bantu man in a truck to the rain forest to hunt the elephants."

"How did you come here—here to this place?"

"The work I did was evil work. I was running from the memory of you, I wanted to find you, and I needed money to survive. I did not know where I was going. I made traps to catch the elephants for their ivory. It did concern me in my sleep, that evil work I did. I finally left that work. When I found the way to the coast, I met an Ibo man who knew the ways of the world. He took me north, taught me English, and brought me to this country as his servant."

She looks at him, admiring his lean tall physique. He is so tall and handsome. When she had first married him he was tall and lean with a boyish face, almost effeminate—he was effeminate at that time she thinks affirmatively, with his young face attached to a tall body. She did not find him appealing at that time because of his bizarre appearance. And she would deride him verbally because of it. Time had put girth at his waist that was not fat of any kind but of muscle and power. She could see this even though he has not removed his parka. His presence is masculine and his voice is heavier than when she had married him—time having given it the sound of a lion's soft roar at dusk as he converses with her. The hair at his face is black and knotted. It is hair that grows at every inch on his face that hair can grow, and it is black as coal. His hands have grown thick, meaty, and callused. Thick, meaty, independent living entities they are. Hands that can work alone, it seems, without his command, and move great objects, heavy objects her hands cannot move. His mental integrity seems to be well suited before his arrival here in this land, it came to her, and only her purpose at this time has caused him to become uncertain. Her womanly ingenuity helps her feel this inside.

"But how did you come here?" she asked him.

"That Ibo was a good man. We traveled the world together. He showed me places that a man from the desert would have never known existed. My eyes were big with surprise about all that was around me. He educated me while I worked for him. When it came that he did not know enough to teach me, he sent me to a school at night. From that way I went to the university and graduated in this country. When he died it was as my father had died again, and I came here to fly the oil workers about the state.

"Your brother told me how your father died. I am sorry about it."

"It could have been worse. The blood that came from my father's mouth was from old age. Whenever I find my heart is heavy with pain, I think of our brothers and sisters in our country who have never even known their fathers, and I become ashamed of my pain. I was a lucky one; such as yourself; your parents still live."

"I am still in your heart Tashelo; I am immemorial inside you? Can you understand me? Do you still care for a desert woman? I want you to come back with me. I have money now and a farm with animals. I have people working for me. I have property not only in our land but land in other places in the world. It will not be like it was in the past. I am lonely for you. There is not a day that does not pass that I wish I could turn back time and really appreciate you then as I do now. Is it not true that you were 19 and I was only 13 years old? I did not know you at the water well; you were a strange man to me. I was only there to collect water with my friend. The next day you were at my village with your mother and father, asking my mother and father to let you marry me. I ran from the village on our wedding night

The Fish Hunter

to sleep in the bush. I would have stabbed myself with a poison arrow, or done anything not to marry you. Just say you will not walk from me and not come back with me. I was crazy Tashelo. I was only a child."

"I am grateful to see you. When you say you were young, you tell me no falsehood. You were young. You did not stab yourself. After our marriage I was like a father in my thinking towards you. You came to trust me. Yes, you did run through the bush back to your family's village. But I was like a father in my thinking, and I went back to get you, and you trusted me. You were my wife.

"When I took you with me to work for the Tswana, I did not think that you would leave me for one of them because of the money he carried in his pockets. For three years we had laid together as husband and wife. I was to work in the fields and you were to work in the house of his mother. You were 16 years old Nukie. Our marriage had become complete."

The interior of the cabin has become warmer, and the man takes off his parka and places it over the chair that sits across from her at the table. He is a monument to her eyes, so huge, so muscular. She realizes how foolish she had been to leave a man such as he. He has indeed turned out to be such a wonderfully made creature. She pinches herself with her fingers for her lewdness and concentrates on her purpose for coming such a distance.

The man sees a thick layer of dust on the table; he realizes the woman is trying to avoid the dust by sitting erect and not leaning upon the table with her elbows. He takes a large blue handkerchief sprinkles with white patterns of squares and triangles from his pocket, he stands to wipe the presence of the dust away, places the handkerchief on the table, sits himself comfortably in the chair in front of her with his hands behind his head, and looks at her with melancholy eyes, but eyes electric with thoughts of the past and the future.

Memoirs of a Taxi Driver

"Our marriage was complete Tashelo; you are correct. But there was no man between you and me. I had no love for that Tswana inside me. I only saw a way to help you and me in the world. There was food and bread and other resources that we did not have that the Tswana had. He gave me blankets, and his mother gave me tobacco. You must realize I did that for you and me."

"Nukie, my heart felt inside that something was wrong between you and the Tswana. You cannot tell me that there was nothing between you and him. When you did not leave that job and come back to our village in the desert bush, I brought that concern to the Tswana headman. He told you that your place was with your husband. I was your husband. Was I not your husband? Did you leave with me to return to our village? No, you did not leave with me. We had everything the bush could provide for us. Our people have lived on the land for many thousands of years. We were beholden to no one. Only if your mind is corrupted do you believe that their food and clothing is important."

"Tashelo, I did leave with you. We both went back to our village."

"Yes, we did go back. But you would leave me and go back to the Tswana and work for him without me. That I told to the Tswana headman. I told to him that you lay down with that man for the blankets and tobacco he gave you. You always had tobacco. The headman asked you if you were lying with the Tswana man you worked for, and you and he lied in front of the Tswana headman. You knew, if you had told the truth to the Tswana headman, you would have been beaten, and you did tell a lie. You must be honest with me now. You have come back for me, and I feel a falsehood in you now. I do not feel a lie in you; I know that the lie is in you.

"Then Nukie, you made arguments with me because of my suspicions, and you went to live in the house of the Tswana. Do you think I do not have reason in my mind to suspect you? You stay with him for months; you do not

124

The Fish Hunter

come home and say that I am not sane in my thinking, when you are the reason for my insane thinking.

"Explain to me now why you would go to Johannesburg and then to Europe with that rich Tswana and leave me for 17 years with no wife to lie with, to talk to, or have a family with? Nothing happened between you and the Tswana for the 17 years we have been apart? Please have respect for my thinking Nukie."

The woman rises for the first time from the seat and walks unconsciously pass the man with her eyes looking out the window behind him. There is urgency in her mind as she evaluates the severity of the charges. She speaks no word and walks to the window and sees Whitefish standing at attention not 20 feet away from the cabin. She thinks how lovely the dog is in its attentiveness. There is an almost childlikeness in its behavior. The animal seems to be distressed and ready to depart with its master she thinks. The dog reminds her of the noises she heard one early spring afternoon while waiting for a bus in Paris. The season was new, and birds flitted and whistled in every tree. Then there was the noise of a distressed child. When she went to investigate, it was a child standing at a school door entrance with his school bag and comrades a long time gone away from him. When she asked in the little French she spoke what the tears were about, the child told her that his mother was supposed to pick him up, but she had not come, and he was all alone. Standing next to the child for some minutes, she attempted to comfort him. They both did not hear a car drive up. The car's horn made its sound, and the child ran from her to the car that awaited him. She thinks of the child's small round face and sighs. Her breath at the cold window becomes like an ectoplasmic image of the child's face. She wonders if the child still remembers her and that moment in time. She stands there for a few minutes lost in her muse.

Looking away she sees the bird not looking at her. It is such a large creature. Her eyes stay on the creature for not a long time. This bird has no importance to her. Her only concern is the mission in the cabin at the moment. How can she get this desert man to come with her without losing him forever to the faith of the land she stands upon? She unbuttons the wolf coat that has made the calf-high boots she wears invisible, now cognizant to any eyes that are present. The coat makes her warm. She comes from her torpor, turns and walks back to the table, committed to have a more Arcadian tone in her voice, attempting to disparage the importance of her mission inside herself. However, as she reaches the wooden chair next to the wooden table, her cheerful substance fails her, and emotion reveals itself in her eyes and face. A tear comes to her voice.

"My darling one, it is true that I did not want you to be mine before we married, but time did change that. My heart did grow for you. I saw how we lived compared to the Tswanas and wanted the home life that they themselves had. To live in a hut with the sand next to me was not the life that I wanted after living with the Tswana family.

"I saw that their way was that we worked for them and they not for us. I could only see that if we could possess their life, it would help you and me. But it did evolve into more then that. I became greedy for the more that was around me. There were the books and places in the world that opened my eyes and made them hungry for more than the lizards we ate and the mongongo groves we harvested. When I came back to our hut I found something missing, and you could not see my thoughts of a better life. A border grew between us because of that knowledge that I had learned from the Tswana as you worked in the fields that made their land profitable.

"I did not want to live in the desert with skin dry to the sun and with dirt under my fingernails. I wanted to live the life of a Tswana and the others that I had seen and heard of that did not live in our land. I asked to be taken to Johannesburg and to France and to the Netherlands where the dams prevent the sea from entering. The things I did

The Fish Hunter

with the son of the Tswana woman were done for you and me. There was nothing of importance between the Tswana man and I.

"I did not hate the Tswana man or love him, but he showed me the world I saw was good and that I wanted. It is in the dammed country by the sea that I worked and made the money that kept me alive and paid for my education after the Tswana man had left me alone there. And when I sent word of you there was no word. You had gone from our land, and no members of our families knew your place in the world. It was not easy, but I did that and prospered with much work. Now I have wealth, the life I have dreamt of, the money to support us in the ways the Tswanas support themselves, and I also now have the means that others from outside our bush country support themselves. Because of my success, it is because of me, that your own brother, sister, and their children are supported with jobs I have made available to them."

The man, comfortable in the chair in front of her, understanding her, leans forward dissolving that position for one that affords him to lean with both arms at the table as he beckoned her to sit in front of him. She is exceedingly feminine to him and small in height. Her eyes are slightly slanted in her ebony face. She is a woman of his kind. The blood of this woman and those before her caused his people to procreate sufficiently for thousands of years up until today. He wonders how such a small fragile woman, a woman he could kill with one powerful blow from his fist, be so valuable, so essential, yet so painful to mankind. She is the power of his people he thinks inside his mind, the backbone of their existence, and the food of their survival.

She affectionately places her open hand at the side of his face as she sits, and it is small as that of a girl young in her youth, with the simple redolence of sweet perfume. As she sits at his command, he does everything not to hold her hand and kiss the goodness that it contains in its existence before him and looks away to remove it from his face. But, without his conscious understanding, he takes possession of it and kisses the hand, holding it to his mouth as a hungry beast to eat from it the repast that is to besot him to her as Samson was to Delilah, like a beast that is gentle during supper to the kind hand that feeds it, he begins to bite at the soft tissue at her hand with his teeth, alternating with kisses and biting to consume the goodness that it also possesses. Turning the small palm finally to his face, he places his warm lips inside it to taste its sweetness.

"Yes Nukie, you are still good in my heart. Every moment without my arms about you makes me hungrier for you. I thought as I came closer to the cabin with the dogs in the snow that I could be strong against you, but every moment with you causes me to know that this effort to be strong is impossible."

Holding his hand tightly, she leans forward to the edge of her chair and kisses his hand.

"Oh Tashelo, it is painful for me also."

He releases her small hand to stand and walk away from her. He stands at the window to look out into the forest pass the dogs and the fish hunter with it wings now open to the wind.

"I cannot go back with you now Nukie. I can never go back with you to the desert. I have been too long in this land. The woman I have at the cabin waits for me to return. I cannot leave her. She has been good to me."

"Tashelo, the Pakistani has told me of that woman you lie with. I understand you have grown close to her. I know you have grown use to hearing her voice and touch. But I am a woman of your people. It is I who loves you. You chose me from all the women in our land. That means something. My skin is black and my loin will bear you many strong children as our forefathers and foremothers before us. That woman cannot do this with her flaxen hair and blue eyes. We are the real people in the world. Place your love in me, place your children in me, and our people will carry on into the future as they should."

The Fish Hunter

"How shall I say to her that I will be leaving her? She will cry. I will have to drag her across the snow, for she will not let go of me as I leave."

"Just leave with me now. The Pakistani man and the plane will be arriving soon Tall One. Leave the dogs. The Pakistani will come back to retrieve them and take them back to her.

He ponders what she is saying, visualizing in his mind the steps he would take and the bridges that would be burned to execute her plan. She slowly perambulates from her chair to stand behind him at the window to encourage his thoughts to depart with her. She cannot see the dogs through the window behind his tall shoulders but sees the fish hunter in the tree with its majestic-self unharmed by the cold. Her eyes are not interested in this bird-king, and she speaks to Tashelo as only a woman knows how.

"I am yours, and you are mine. Did you not sit in front of our hut as my husband? Did I not put you to sleep at night in the way only a Zhun/twa woman could?"

He places his thumb to his mouth to bite at the nail, pondering, thinking. With his iron hands and iron arms he turns to her to possess her at her shoulders and pulls her towards him like a lifeless, weightless doll and places his giant forehead to her small forehead. She is very beautiful; and she is in his heart. But then he thinks of all the pain she had caused him, how he had searched for her secretly, helping her in her quests, far off in the distance unbeknownst to her as she worked. He turns away and walks over to the table noticing the dust that he had missed with his handkerchief and thinks about the woman waiting for his return as the afternoon sun begins to leave.

He remembers how Whitefish had held on to the grizzly and would not let go. He thinks about how no one had told him about the grizzly-king with its fur so thick, its back so silver, and its body so strong, that a pistol with six bullets could not, would not, stop. That those bullets would be like toy stones against its body. It was that Russian woman who

Memoirs of a Taxi Driver

had placed the knife through the thick strong fur, into the thick strong heart of the grizzly-king many times. It had been her that had sat by him interminably through the night while he did not know the world around him, and it was her tears and voice he had heard when his life came back to him.

He turns, walks to the window, and walks back to the table to place his parka over his broad shoulders.

"I cannot return to the desert with you. My place is here now. I cannot leave; it is impossible."

His words roll over her like some large train unexpected from a mountain tunnel. She knows she is losing him, her eyes bug open, they become moist in front of him, she kindly take him by his shoulders and she speaks softly to him.

"The headman never gave us a divorce. You are my husband. Yes you will return with me. I am your wife. You married me. You are not going to stay here. I have looked and looked for you. Everything I have done I have done for us. I had no pleasures from my work. I only saw that I could bring you and myself up in the world by what I did. The Tswana took me to Europe; he showed me Europe, and he left me. But I survived, and I am here for you now. You are my husband. I have enough money for me; I have enough for you; I have enough money for your family. Your family works for me."

"Nukie, I am grateful for what you have done. You are in my heart. Time cannot take that away from me. Go back to our place and find a new husband for yourself, and let us live in our minds the past we had together. So much has changed now. I have done my duty to you. I have helped you. Leave this place and never come back. The lake will be frozen soon, and there will be no way the plane will be able to land on floats if you stay longer."

Her eyes become large in their sockets, larger than he could ever remember seeing them. She holds tightly to his parka with her girl-fingers disappearing into the fur.

The Fish Hunter

"Help me! How do you mean help me? It is I who helps you! I feed your brother and sister! I feed their children! They come to me! When your nephew became ill, I paid his hospital bill. I did that for you and me! I have come to this ice place with my own money to find you and to bring you back to a good life! You were nothing in our land but a desert person, living in a desert hut. I did not want to live like that after I found how the real world was. Why should I walk through sand when I can ride across pavement? Leave this place and come back with me. The plane should be here in 30 minutes."

The man turns to open the cabin door, but she is quick and strong for a small woman and slams the door with a great force and secures it with her back. This causes the dogs to stand and look at the cabin. The bird is startled, raises itself with one movement of its wings to take itself to a spruce a safer distance from the domestic animals and humans. There are more sounds that come from the cabin, and a woman's voice is heard with screams behind it. The door opens and quickly closes with a loud report. This causes all the dogs to stand and some to bark. The fish hunter with an ochre eye, so sharp, so precise, watches without its equanimity disrupted. Suddenly there is a quiet in the forest and in the cabin.

The woman with her small frame tries to move the man back from the door to the chair. The man is astounded at the strength of the woman and relents to her will. He sits down childlike and crosses his legs to calm her. She is breathing hard and she stands over him

"Tashelo, you are going with me. The plane will be here in a few minutes. I am taking you with me."

"Nukie, sit down for one minute, and let me explain to you."

She knows that she cannot stop him, so she sits down, hoping if she does he will not resist her and give her a few minutes maybe to change his mind. She leans forward and places her face in the palms of her hands, with her elbows at

131

Memoirs of a Taxi Driver

her knees to support her arms. She wets her lips with her tongue and leans back exhausted in her chair. The man sees how tired she is and removes his coat so as to comfort her. He speaks softly to her.

"Nukie, this is good what you are doing now. But it is too late now. Go back; find a husband for yourself. You must not think that I do not care for you in my heart. I do care for you. It is too late now. I have obligations here now. My life is with this country. The years have been too many here."

"It will never be too late for the one who has married a woman. One who has stood in public and said 'yes' in front of my mother and father. I am your wife. No headman has said we were divorced."

"Nukie, it is the actions of the wife that says a divorce is true and final. I did my duty to you. I waited for you. I went to get you. When you would not come back, I went to the Tswana headman and told him of your ways with that other man. When you left and went away, my heart tried to find you, and, when my heart did find you, I took care of you."

The woman laughs softly.

"How could you take care of me in the desert. I was living a life of a civilized person. I was not in the desert."

"Nukie, yes I was living in the desert. We were once living in the desert, but we were rich when we lived there. It is all in the mind about riches."

"Tashelo, stop thinking like a bum. Come back now. Look where you are living. You are living in a shack. I have a house now, with plumbing. You have no plumbing. You are not worth a nickel. I am saving you man. You live in the woods."

"Yes, I live in the woods, but I live here because I choose to. I could live on the Riviera or in Manhattan if I so chose."

"Listen to me boy. You are nothing. Come home now. You could not live in those places if you dreamed about them. I take care of your brother; I take care of your sister; I will take care of you."

The Fish Hunter

The man sits and stares into the woman's eyes without blinking. And when the time passes into minutes without him looking away, the woman looks away from him. His nostrils flare and beads of sweat are coming from his forehead. His upper lip trembles and his tongue finally comes from between his lips to wet them.

"Nukie, it is true that you were my wife and that my heart was complete for you. Many years did pass, and you did not come back to me. Everyday was as though a week had passed, and I waited for your silhouette to come through the desert darkness to our campfire and to our hut, but that never happened. My father many times before his death told me to forget about you and to find a new wife for myself. I only wanted you, and I could not be happy with anyone else. I sat for over two years hoping and wishing for your return to no avail. One day I decided to go out and find you.

"Money was and has never been important to me Nukie. I was born a Zhun/twa. We live from the things that grow above and below the land; we hunt the animals that walk the land. When I had you, my life was complete. When you left, pain was in me all the time. I told my people that I would ride with a Bantu man to the north for only a few months work. I did not tell them that I went to find you. Our people know that the world is big now and that my search for you would be impossible. I did leave with that man, and we went to the rain forests of the north. There I hunted the elephant and rhino for its ivory and other body parts illegally. That did not sit well in my heart, and I left that to carry the supplies for the researchers that came to those forests to study the plants and wildlife that lived within its borders. Death almost took me away two times on my trek through the forest; and two times I came away from it still alive. My feet became infected as will happen in a forest with rain much of the time. But I persevered. It is in that way, through the forest and across the plains that I came to the ocean.

Memoirs of a Taxi Driver

"At the villages that lie near the ocean I looked for work that I, a man, could find. I, this one man, did not find work until I found a man that had been injured by a fall from a cliff to the ground. That Ibo man was in the business of diamonds, emerald, and rubies that are apart of the Congo. I did not know about these worldly things. It was not until later that I found that he was thought to have some of those resources with him and was attacked for them. I climbed down to that man who was not old but in great pain. There I built him a fire and helped to repair his leg and hunted for food and brought him water until I could go to find help for him. That Ibo man was a rich man in the world and was grateful to me. He took me on as a servant and brought me into the world outside the continent.

"He traveled the world, and I was by his side. He being an older man, with his wife being dead without having any children for him, took me as a son to some degree, which became consummated with time. When he died, I knew his business as a son, and his legacy he did leave behind for me.

"As you know, I went back to our land to find you. And you were not to be found. Your mother and father showed me the things you had sent them. My father died as I had come, but I did not go back as a rich man but as that man that had left my land. Money was never important to me. I had money then, but I did not have you. I could not really be happy. Because of that money I had many people working for me.

"From the family of the Tswana man that had stolen you from me, I had heard that you were in France. It was in France that I went to follow you and I did not find you, but I found your trail. In that way I found that you had gone to the country to the north that builds walls to protect itself from the sea. From city to town and from village to suburb I searched for you.

"I first went to Rottendam, a city rebuilt from the war and on to The Hague with no clue of you. To the east of Arnhem across the German border I went to hear that you had been

The Fish Hunter

there but had gone to Amsterdam. I walked the streets and looked in the directories until I found nothing and hired the people that could find you. After having found you, I found you in the Wallen as you sat in a window to sell yourself to the men that walked by that might find you attractive.

"I stood off to one side so that you might not recognize me and watched you. My heart was heavy with pain, and I left the Wallen to leave the country. I changed my thinking and decided not to leave and to confront you about your filthy work, but when I came upon your window I did not have the decision in my mind to know what to say to you. I did not want you anymore in my life, but something kept me near you.

"I set up an Amsterdam office to operate my business, and at night I would walk the street with the others as tourist and customers but away from you so that you could not know me as your husband. I could not decide how I would come to you. One day I decided to come to you on the street as a happenstance while you shopped but changed that thinking also. It was through my efforts that I found the owner of the building and brothel that you worked and bought the building. Through my attorneys I agreed that your boss should go to you with an offer to sell the building, and, along with the building, the brothel at low financing to you. Because your boss was doing it the way I had wanted, I told him I would compensate him for any lost he might incur. It was very expensive the way it was done, but it was done that way.

"My business is very large, and at times I would have to leave the country for a few months for the States. When I would return, I would go to your place of business to watch at a distance its progress. I one day set myself down and came to the realization that I still cared for you and that I would get you out of the business you were in. I had my attorneys go to you with the proposal to buy the building from you at a very expensive price that would be enough to have you retire if you wanted to do that thing.

Memoirs of a Taxi Driver

"When you did not want to do that, I had my attorneys leave without discussion. Some months later they did go back and offered you enough that only a crazy one would refuse. As you remember, I had them have you agree on paper that you would not open another brothel in the country. I only hoped that you would settle down and not include yourself in that type of business again.

"I stayed in Amsterdam until I found that you had bought a small cottage outside of Lelystad. I would drive by your cottage to observe you but that never happened. You were no place to be found. I found, after some time, that you were back visiting our land, and after your trips became a regular event for you, I would send the people that worked for me to find what work you did there. I was told that you had settled there with land that you owned and people that you employed. When that was settled in my mind, I closed my office in Amsterdam, moved my office to London, and I came here to this place and through events met that woman that waits for me at night. Here is where I stay now, and with the Pakistani I fly the people about in the state to the far off tundra that is all about this ice. I have money, but no one knows this money is had by a desert man in an ice place."

"You helped me? It was you that sent those attorneys?"

"Yes, I helped you. I loved you."

The woman looks down with feline eyes to a floor dusty with time and contemplates what has been surrendered to her with a voice that was not opaque in its allegory, but one that spoke with veracity that only a man with knowledge of the events or one man with magical powers or some innate power using him as a conduit would know. She looks through the window out into the pines that surround the cabin and sees the darkness enveloping the sky with the baldheaded bird perched near the dead-wood tree as its brethren seem to stand as sentries around one which once was fresh and strong, once strong as they themselves were now. A one that withstood the passing of time but now has

The Fish Hunter

succumbed to the ferocity of the North and now its deceased and empty frame prepares to fall to the earth, the earth that will consume its remains into cytoplasmic, protoplasmic elements. They seem to solute their fallen brother, this fallen comrade still standing, with its once new and fertile wood, its now near petrified frame, with its branches reaching out into the advancing shadows that will turn the day into the thick dark night, that is now the thick dark color its wood now possesses, making it one with the night, dead with the night.

She looks down at the floor and looks befuddled away from it. She stands and walks to the window to hide her face that now shows her nakedness to him. How can she make her face descent to him in her explanations to him?

Her brow had become moist with sweat on that first day. She lay in front of the man on her back with hard gleaming breasts. She was uncomfortable on her back with her secret places exposed as the man undressed. She could see in the large walled mirror the small pinkness of her vagina with its volutes damp, and the taut cincture of her anus waiting for the paying man. The man set down at the side of the bed grinning and joggled her petite thighs with his large hands.

How is she to excuse her behavior? Her past away from him is exposed as a child at birth without a blanket to protect it from the cold of the world. His eyes are the world to her. He is the world to her. When the Tswana man left her, she was homeless with little money. "Maybe that excuse is not good enough; he may not believe that," she thought. She was too embarrassed to go back home. Would he believe I was forced into my situation? Maybe he will understand that? Will those explanations be enough?

She knew with this story he has told her he had dashed her away from him. She is embarrassed. She searches for more explanations to escape, explain the facts that have been bestowed upon her. She looks at the bird near the dead tree."

"Tashelo, the bird in the tree outside this window, it is an eagle?"

Tashelo gets up from his seat and walks over to the window to look out at the bird with Nukie.

"That is a bald eagle".

"How does it eat? How does it live in such a place as this? There is no life here I can see."

"It is a fish hunter. It eats mainly fish in the lakes and rivers and other small mammals about the forest. It lives from the land as we did once. A car and money would not sustain this bird. The land with its resources is all it needs."

"There are no fish in our desert, is there Tashelo?"

"There are no fish in our desert, but it is free as we were. It eats mainly from the water, we ate mainly from the mongongo groves."

She turns to him and places her small hands at his arms.

"I did not ask you to do those things. I would have succeeded without you Tashelo. It was a way of making money. People do deceitful things everyday to make money. That is common. I am not perfect. I used the money to study at the university. All of the money I earned went for a good purpose. I am educated. I would have been successful anyway."

"Yes you are educated Nukie, but you must watch what you become in the pursuit of what you want in life."

"I have become a good woman. Yes, I have worked in a brothel, but I was a good person. Look at what I am doing with my money. Come back home. You are my husband. We will have a family. We will have a little boy and a little girl.

"Do you think I would have a little boy and a little girl with you Nukie. Your constitution is not stable. What if I died and there was no more money? Would you place our daughter in a brothel to keep those material goods you long for? We had everything we needed in the desert; no man owned us. We were free as this eagle behind you now. We lived from the land. We went and came as we pleased."

The Fish Hunter

She does not turn to look at the bird, but places her hands down beside her. They cause an old broom to fall to make a noise inside and outside the cabin. The dogs who had been watching the window stood up anticipating the door to open after hearing the broom fall, and the snow under their paws breaks, making the sound of dogs preparing to take flight through the snow. They stand for some minutes and sit and lay down in no particular order. Tashelo does not see the woman's jaw become tight with anger. She stands before him as a warrior princess ready to do battle.

"The plane will be coming in a very few minutes. I want you to come. Leave the animals here. I love you."

"I can not go, my Little Fox. I have done my duty to you as a husband."

"You are coming, you are coming! Do you hear me, you dirty spy?

She raises her left fist into the air and pounds it into the base of his neck above the shoulder. When this does not move him, she takes her right hand to hold him and pounds his shoulder--being careful not to strike him in a more vital area.

Her arm stops in the air suddenly with his thick powerful fingers wrapped around her wrist to control her. Tashelo takes her right hand and peels it away from his parka to holds her arms out and away from her body like that of hands on a clock, and he pulls her into him to make her plumose frame invisible within his arms and broad chest. He feels her breast at his chest soft and firm. He pulls her even closer to prolong the thought of her against him and kisses her throat and face, and she can hear the tears that follow the emotion that is actual and sincere. She desists and listens.

"Nukie, the one my heart is complete for, you will always be here inside of me, but I cannot go back with you. Go back to the desert and live a life without me. This is my home; this is my place now. Someone waits for me."

Memoirs of a Taxi Driver

Tashelo turns and opens the door to the cabin, and the dogs stand at attention to receive him. The woman without a coat runs after him into the cold and grabs him. The fish hunter moves off to some distance to watch the two humans. When this did not stop the tall man, she jumps up on his back still holding him and struggles with him without words. Far into the forest, quite a distance away from the cabin, there is the sound of two humans grunting and breathing in the fall cold of the North, and the snow becomes compacted under scuffling boots.

A second time the fish hunter moves off to some distance to watch the two humans. It cocks its head to watch and opens it wings to balance itself against the wind.

Tashelo finally manages to expel her from his back and turns to face her. Nukie's breaths come out of her and hang for long moments in the air, and her eyes are bugged. She regains her grip at his Parka.

"No, No, come back Tashelo."

"Go back Nukie. Go back home."

The sound of a plane causes them both to look in the direction of the lake. The size of the plane makes it appear as a paper plane, fragile to the mountains surrounding it.

"The Pakistani comes now. Go home Nukie. I cannot leave this place."

She lets him remove her hands from him and stands in the cold not cognizant of it and looks into his chest as he turns to leave. The man gives a command and the dogs become ready. He steps towards the sleigh, grabs at its handles and concomitantly unties its anchoring rope. He gives a loud report; and the dogs are off down a forest path.

As the befuddlement leaves the woman, she becomes aware that the man is leaving, and she turns and runs after the man into the forest calling after him. She falls and lifts herself again to run and stumbles on into the forest until she disappears amongst the spruce pines as they stand silently against the darkening sky.

140

The Fish Hunter

The fish hunter looks down as a king upon the open door of the cabin and the forest trail that disappears into the trees. It cocks its head several times to the right and left. The night darkness approaches. The bird opens its wings to secure its balance as a gush of wind rocks its throne under it. There is no sound but that of a plane as it lands in the lake. It pulls up to the dock and its motor becomes quiet. The bird opens its wings to the wind and the wind carries it gracefully backwards over the green-pine cones. With several beats of its wings it moves slowly forwards into the late afternoon away to the south. The wings take the bird higher over dogs stopped in the snow on a command from their master. Behind the sleigh a man and a shivering woman stand embraced. There is still time to cover many miles before the night envelopes the land completely. At a mountain a last tall sharp wedge of sunlight hangs defiantly against the approaching night.

One Afternoon

I am an attorney now. I have been one for thirty-five years. It was a career I had wanted since I was a child and old enough to know what an attorney was. I really worked at it. While in law school I had a husband and young child at home, and I had to drive a taxi to make life comfortable for us while he was still in school. There was not a lot of time for my husband or my daughter, and there were days that I did not procrastinate and left out without a word to either after I woke from a deep sleep to leave for work.

One afternoon, a long time ago, I was deep in the heart of our fair city when she stopped me. She was in her early fifties with ample locks of graying hair. Unsmiling, she asked me to drive to a cemetery not far away. Upon entering the gates she directed me up and down the paths expertly, almost surgically.

Her face was melancholy and strained as she gazed out of the passenger's window, seeming to be in deep and abysmal thought, not wanting to relive what she was thinking but remembering. She spoke to me not.

She asked me to begin slowing down and commanded a complete halt when we reached her destination. I did not behold the roses in her hand until she disembarked and

One Afternoon

walked to the stone amongst the many. Kneeling and placing the roses at the stone, I saw her speaking, praying softly...quietly.

I waited a few minutes and decided to stretch my legs. I made a wide and not so suspicious circle about the woman and saw the deceased had died some time ago. It seemed to be a child. The years were few in number. With even more care, I quietly returned to my taxi and patiently waited until she finished. She asked me to take her back to the corner she flagged me at earlier. As we rode back, she seemed to have the same sadness about her, upon her, but she held her head higher with a smile, not a smile that you and I could see, but a burden appeared to have been raised from her for a short time.

Not speaking, she paid me. She disappeared into the crowd that surrounded my cab.

Whenever I drive by that cemetery, I think about that woman, that day, so long ago. I think of how immense her love must have been to take a taxi regularly, I suppose, to visit that loved one.

That evening, when I arrived home, my husband was sitting at the kitchen table deep into his studying, and without locking the door I went over to him and lifted him from his chair and held him and placed my nose in his hair to smell him. He asked me what was the concern in me, and I only pulled him closer and held him a little longer.

When I saw my daughter sitting at her coloring books on the floor, I released my husband and went to my daughter and placed her in my lap and kissed her many times and looked into her eyes, far into her eyes, and ran my fingers through her hair to savor every moment of her that God had given me.

To Kill a Cop

"I am a murderer. It is rare that people murder one another, but it happens that people do murder one another. Some murders are justified and others are not. I murdered a man. It was justified. Is it not true that they tried to murder Hitler? No one could ever tell me that the murder I did was not justified. Why did I do it, and how did it begin in my mind to do that murder? I shall answer that question. I shall tell you the story that caused me to murder a man.

"It all started when I was a little boy in the city—not the murder, but the love I had inside for my brother. Murder was the last thing on my mind then, but in time my whole life would revolve around the murder of that man. It was because of my brother I murdered him, not a woman, not money, but my only brother.

"After my brother and I were born, my parents had no other siblings for my brother and me. My brother was my best friend, but like any brothers growing up together, we would have fun and arguments. But we did almost everything together, and we went almost everywhere together. I do not remember when I became cognizant of my younger bother's presence around me. At this moment I

144

To Kill a Cop

can only remember a photograph of him on the living room sofa my mother showed me, and the time that he lay in our bedroom helpless as a child.

"My brother was a gentle child. I remember falling down on my knee tearing the flesh open on it, and how my brother at six years old set next to me and cried. He ran his hands through my hair, and told me not to cry. It was a thick soft child-like hand that children only have at that age. I smile inside almost all the time whenever I think about him that day, telling me not to cry, and he was crying. He was a bright student, much better in books than I was. If it had not been for my bother, I probably never would have finished grammar school on time. He was so patient with me. I was so stupid.

"We use to play with glass marbles. One spring season my brother won all of my marbles from me. I had not one marble in my possession. But he had a kind heart, and he lent me one marble to use until I could win some back from him. He did not have to do that, but he did. He was just that kind of person. As a matter-of-fact, knowing him as I did, he definitely let me win some marbles from him so that I could continue to play.

"My brother was a better-looking child than I was. Whenever my mother took us to church, all the women would point him out and compliment her on how handsome he was. I never got any praises from the females I can remember. That never bothered me though. I loved my brother. I knew he was handsome, and I knew he was more inclined academically than I was. I found him admirable and tried my best to excel. I never had any jealousy of him while we were growing up. I was proud to be with him.

"I was almost four years older than my brother. When we started to date girls, he could always get the beautiful girls, even though he was only fourteen years old and did not have any money. Girls just loved him. He had charisma and personality. But he would never go out with any girl unless she had a friend for me. She had to be pretty. If she was not a pretty girl, the girl he was dating could not even call our house. He really had a way with girls and never abandoned me.

"About a year before he was shot and murdered, we were coming from a grocery store. We were waiting for the traffic light to change from red to green. As we proceeded through the light, the car on my left that was supposed to have stopped for the light did not stop, and while I was looking at my brother on my right side, I did not see the car continue to roll on. But my brother saw the car rolling towards me and pulled me back at my collar, and the car hit a woman and killed her. It could have been me that day and not that woman. He saved my life.

"There was only one thing wrong with my brother that annoyed me. That annoyance I attribute to his age. He was frisky as a puppy, and he ran around like he had ants in his pants. We would be walking down the street together, and while talking to me he would be running in front of me and talking while walking backwards and then carrying on the same conversation while walking in back of me jumping onto my back. That guy never got tired; he was always running around.

"The night that my brother was murdered I was not with him. As I said, we were almost always together. But I was studying that evening for an examination that I had the next day. I was supposed to be graduating from high school that spring, and I wanted to make sure that I passed the examination without being concern about the grade not being sufficient.

"There were rapid knuckle raps at the door from someone, but I paid no attention, my mother was there, she would answer it I thought. I knew her walk with her house slippers making their sounds as she left the kitchen for the front door of the house. What stopped me from my reading was the rapid talk, a scream from my mother, and my mother's emergency call to me. We both followed the boy who had come to the door, running down the street, leaving the door

To Kill a Cop

unlocked and not preparing our person's for the eyes of the world. We ran through an alley and down the gangway of two buildings with my mother screaming and howling like I had never seen or heard before when she saw my brother lying with blood encircling his head. She told me to call the police. I knew she meant an ambulance because the police was already there, standing around.

"In those days the police would and could shoot a person if he was running away from them. On that night my brother was standing between two brownstones with some other boys that night. It happened like it does in any large city, a covey of teenage boys standing in the gangway between two buildings talking and laughing. They could have looked suspicious. However, when the police did arrive my brother was the one who ran. He ran and was shot in the back of the head from what was told to me over and over again by those who had been there. He did not die right away. He was in a coma. The other boys were arrested on a false police report written by both officers involved. On their court date I went to the court with my parents and my brother's friends, and they pointed the officer out to me who had shot my brother. My eyes stayed on that man and did not forget that man. I hated that cop, and my forehead and palms were wet with sweat from the hate. Tears were all over my face that day.

"I could not listen to the minutiae that went on in the court but only looked at that man who had shot my brother. He was in his early twenties I supposed, still slim and not a tall man with blond hair. In court his uniform was crisp and sharp. I had never seen a uniform so well taken care of. I never forgot his face. In any crowd I would be able to recognize his face.

"I was only nineteen when my brother finally died in the hospital. I was devastated, my parents were devastated, our lives were never the same because of what happened after my brother was shot and finally died. The city did settle with us with a financial package, but it was not enough for the loss of my bother. No amount of money would be restitution for a loss so great. When my brother died is when I finally made up my mind to kill that licentious human animal. I dropped out of the university and drove a taxi to make ends meet. I never made enough money to finally move away from my parents. I just lived with them, and I changed into a silent man with problems inside my head about the murder of my brother. I was not a drunkard or illegal substance abuser as you might think after my only brother was murdered. I was melancholy, and it was almost impossible to get me to laugh about anything. When I laughed, it was a fabricated effort, and my parents and the few friends I had knew that. It took me years to stop crying in my bedroom at night. I even cried on the buses and trains, and I theatrically pretended that I had a head cold in those public places.

"It was five years before I really started to make plans on how I would kill that cop. I had no gun, and I had never killed anyone before. That hate, that contempt for that man just grew forever into me. My brother was dead, and that dirty cop was still walking around alive, eating food, having fun and maybe even married with a family. I wanted to kill him. I would kill him, and I finally decided on how I would do that act.

"As I said before, I never made much money. I only worked when I had to. My brother's death was so devastating to me I had little interest even in girls. I only thought about that dirty cop. I did not even know his name. I knew his face though. I saw him drive by one day some years after my brother's death while I was walking my dog, and that foolish man slowed down and asked me what kind of dog it was. I started to walk away and not answer his question but felt that he might recognize me as someone who did not like cops. I answered his question and was friendly to him until he drove away. I thought how foolish that man was to ask what breed of dog I had, and he had murdered my brother four years earlier. I would kill him. I swore it to myself.

To Kill a Cop

"I never took the dog out for a walk again. I made sure that my parents did that. If that was impossible, and I had to take the dog out for a walk, it would only be in the back yard. I never wanted that cop to see me with that dog again. I did not want my face to be associated with anything in his mind.

"I first had to find out where he lived. During shift changes I would wait outside the police station to see what shift he had. That had to be done secretly. I would wait in my taxi a distance away from the station. I started with the first shift. That was the shift I had spoken to him that day about my dog. I never saw him come in on that shift. So I thought that he was entering the station from the back. So, to make sure, I waited at the back of the station at a distance for a few days to make sure that I did not miss him. I did not see him at any time, and I supposed that he was on vacation, and I waited a month and started my search again. When that did not help me to find that murderer, I assumed that he had been switched to another shift, so I did the same thing with the second and third shifts.

"I still did not find that man and it had been a year of watching at every shift. When I found it to be impossible to find him, I resorted to going into the station to use the telephone at shift changes to see if I could find him, and I did not find him. I realized that man must of retired or been transferred to another district, and there were eighteen districts in my city. I had to search all eighteen districts to find him. But you must understand that I was obsessed with finding that man, and I never had much money, but I would find a way to kill him.

"After four years and looking into every squad car I rolled by, I finally found him in a station on the far south side as a desk sergeant in a station I stopped in, pretending to use the telephone. My heart was excited, and I did not let his eyes see that my eyes saw him, and I spoke on the telephone to no one and pretended to write some important information down that was given to me. All that time my heart fluttered, and the rush of blood to my head made my head light like a feather.

"I was excited and went home that night and went back in the morning to make sure my eyes were not wrong, and my eyes were not wrong when I saw him park his car and go into the station with his uniform. I stepped from my taxi and secretly peeped into the station to see him at his desk.

"During the week, I waited outside the station for him to leave for home; and when he came out of the station I followed him to his home but lost him less than half way to his home because of the traffic and because he was a faster driver, and I was not. Because I knew part of the way he took home, I would wait for him and follow him, until one day he finally came to his home, and I saw him walk from his car to the front door and open it with his key. That was a long process, but I did not want to be discovered by him or anyone who knew him.

"The next morning I drove to his home, and I watched him as he kissed a woman and walked to his car. I followed him to the station he worked at, and after I was satisfied with all that had happened, I made my plans to proceed.

"I knew nothing about the food vending business, but I knew of a man who owned a cart who stood outside a department store and sold hot dogs to the people who came from it into the streets. I asked him if I could work for him, and he told me that his business was only a one-man business and that he could not pay me.

"I went to the local pet shop bought some cages and animals, and I went to the library and borrowed some books on how to run a business of that sort and read them through, and after reading them through again, did so again. I went back to the library and retrieved more books on chemicals, and I read those books through until I knew each page by hard. At first I was not precise enough, and I had to spend more money on animals. But in time I found the correct formula for my victim, and I went back to that man and offered him some money if he would show me how to operate a cart such as his, and he told me he had no time and that if he had the time he would. I made a deal with him and told him I would pay him if he stood next to me and let me service the customers, and he taught me the business under those circumstances. I worked for him during the day and drove the taxi at night to make ends meet.

"After I had learned the business, I made arrangements to buy my own cart, and I retained the proper licenses from the city and county and readied myself for business. I made one last trip to that cop's home address and saw him kiss the same woman as he left for work, and within a week I had my cart with its hotdogs, hot tamales, and polish sausages ready for the public across the street from the police station. I was friendly to all, but I wanted the police officers for my customers so that they would let me stand in front of the station to sell to people who came and went from its confines. I slowly moved my cart closer to the station and even in the winter some officers would come out without a jacket and buy from me. But the murderer who killed my brother would not come out to buy from me, and one day as he walked by I spoke to him and offered him a hot dog at no cost, and he thanked me but told me he was a vegetarian, and my heart left me, and all I had done was for nothing.

"That whole day I was depressed and laid awake through the night trying to find a way to that horrible man, that filthy cop who had killed my brother who was only running away, a child of sixteen, one who had no gun in his possession, but only ran as children of his age would. That murdering dirty animal--I hated him.

"Something did come to me. In my mind I made ready on how I would do that thing, and I did do that thing, and some weeks later I placed a sign on my cart that said I had vegetarian hotdogs and polish sausages. I gave some of those products away to those who would be interested, and one day like magic, like the hope that I had in me, I saw the murderer of my brother, of my only sibling, come from the station without a jacket and money in his hand to purchase a hotdog.

"I was very pleasant to him and told him that since he was a first time customer I would not charge him, but he insisted that I take his money, and I refused him, and he thanked me as he hungrily took a bite of the food I had held for him secretly for many months, and he ran away into the warmth that awaited him in the station.

"That night at home I could not sleep, I was elated. I placed my hands at my face in contentment and tossed and turned all night happy within myself as if I had won a lottery. I counted every hour, and I could not wait until the sun came back so that I could be there next to the man, the animal I hated so much. The next morning I saw him come to the station as I lifted my cart from the van I had purchased, and when the afternoon came he was there with praise for my hotdogs, and on the following day I recommended a polish for him and he ate that polish, and very few days would go by that he was not there at my cart.

"He was a healthy man. His belly did not hang from him, and when he came down the stairs of the station he would hop and skip his way down, and when he walked up those same stairs, he would take two and three at a time to enter the ingress at the top of them. He was a slim man and very neat in his uniform. On some occasions, he would stop and talk to me about his family while making a purchase. He was a nice person, an ordinary person you might meet on the street. He was married, he told me. He had been married for five years, and he told me he and his wife planned to have children. I asked him if he could ever regret having them some day, and, like a man who looked forward to holding children in his arms, he said there would never be any regrets in his mind for having children. Children grow into teenagers, and teenagers grow into adults, I told him, there would be regrets. And he replied that what I said was true. But it was how parents raise their child that was important in the world. You have to take the good with the bad, he told me.

"I could feel my jaw become tight, and I wanted to ask him how he would feel if his son was shot in the back of his head, but I had waited a long time, and I cooled myself and wiped my cart and spoke with him as an acquaintance. I wore sunglasses because I worked out in the sun all during lunch time and near dinner time, but even through the sunglasses I was afraid that he could see through them into the hate that lay beneath them, and I worked as he talked to me, afraid that he would know of my plan. When the occasion mandated, I would cause my brow to be raised with 'oohs' and 'ahs' coming from my throat in disbelief when he made a point in our conversations that required them. No actor I felt could have put on a better performance.

"I felt that I was not getting anywhere with my method, and I started to take my father's pistol with me. I was going to shoot that cop in the head with that pistol. I wanted to do that with that pistol, and more than twenty times I reached for it in the drawer of my cart, but hope, patience, won me over, and I did not place my fingers on it, and I bit my tongue, and the pain and logic brought me to my senses.

"It was a slow process. I did not even notice it until one day I saw him holding on to the banister at the stairs as he walked over to my cart. Then my mind started to think back to how he used to run down the stairs and took two and three steps at a time when ascending them. Now, this cop stepped down the stairs as a man who might have a belly on him or one who was short in his breathe. He came down slowly, and on approaching my cart he breathed in and asked for a vegetarian hotdog and hot tamale. I told him he looked good. And he told me that I probably told that to all the cops. I told him he did and insisted that he did, and he smiled and consumed his meal as he stood next to the cart, and we talked as we frequently did, and upon finishing his

Memoirs of a Taxi Driver

meal he breathed in laboriously and walked back up the stairs as one person burdened with something inside of him.

"That night I went home and could not sleep with the excitement in me. I placed my hands at my face and set up to pray that he would become sick inside and die. I hated that murderer; I wanted to kill that murderer. He was a murderer who shot children who only ran away from him without guns or knives in their hands.

"The next morning I had little sleep to count on. I was there early in the morning, but he did not come to work. In the afternoon he did not come to work, nor did he come into work the next day, nor the next. I became excited inside of myself, and at the end of my time in front of the station I walked inside, pretending to use the telephone and asked about the sergeant. I was told that he was on vacation. My heart went away from me. He had not told me he was going on vacation. But there was still hope, and I did not miss a day at my stand; I waited everyday for his return.

"After two weeks he did return. When he returned he took the steps two and three at a time until they brought him to the entrance. When he stepped down the stairs, he stepped down taking two and three at a time, and sometimes he would skip over to my cart, and my heart became heavy inside of me, and I wanted to reach for the pistol and end it all at that moment, but I bit my tongue and continued on as I had planned.

"Some weeks and months passed, and there were no ill effects to that murderer of children. Then one day, as I had forgotten about it, I saw him walking down the stairs as he held on to the banister to balance his person from falling. He looked unwell. He came over to my cart, and I served him as usual. He told me that he did not feel well at all, and I told him that it was probably because he was not getting enough rest. I told him it would pass, and I told him he looked good, very good. I did not charge him for the sandwich. He took his sandwich to the station, and as he walked away from me I pretended to wash down my cart with a damp cloth but secretly watched him as he laboriously disappeared behind the station doors.

"That evening I was so overwhelmed with joy. I drove my van home without knowing intricately how I had gotten there. My mind was only on the sick one who came to my cart to consume the foods that I made for him. That night I lie awake happy with contentment as a child before Christmas.

"As time went on, his condition became worst. He started to miss some days from work; he started to gain some weight, not much weight, but enough to cause his waist to hang over his belt. One day I heard that he was in the hospital, and on that news I became happier inside and rubbed my hands together with glee. All that day I was happy, all that day I thanked my customers and blessed them with my heart and even gave some sandwiches away because of my glee.

"When he did come back he was healthier in his appearance. He was closer to himself as I had primarily known him, and he came to my cart for a purchase and my brow rose with pretentious excitement. I questioned him with concern and did not ask where he had been, and on that day he looked at me with a shyness or suspicion in his eyes, and I became afraid that he could see the falsehood in my face, and when I got home, I stood in front of the mirror to show my excitement as I would to him and it was not convincing. I practiced for hours and weeks until I was satisfied with myself, and when he came by my cart I would remove my sunglasses and let him see my eyes to make sure that any suspension he might have was only in his imagination—it worried me all the time that he might suspect me.

"As time went by he became even unhealthier, and it became more obvious in his walk and in his eyes. His eyes were sick eyes, and he would miss work quite often. I noticed that whenever he returned that he seemed to be healthier, and as I worked at my cart and at night at home, I would think deeply how I could make my work more efficient with that man. I got a wonderful idea one day. I found a recipe in a cookbook for vegetarian cookies, and I stayed up late at night making vegetarian chocolate chip cookies. They were delicious, and to get my customers to purchase them, I gave them away initially. They became very popular, and whenever the sergeant came down I would on occasion give him a box to take home for a football game or baseball game that I knew he watched on occasion. I did that for several months and my business became more profitable.

"One day, I saw him come down the stairs of the station with legs of an old man. I was happy inside myself, and he told me on his arrival near my cart that some things were wrong with him and that the doctors could not find the cause. He asked for his usual sandwich and I gave it to him, and I refused his money, but he insisted upon paying me. I took his money and insisted that he take some cookies home, and he took them home, and I watched him walk up the stairs with happiness in my heart. I looked at him a long time, and he almost fell backwards down the stairs, and I found myself wishing that he had fallen and his brains had splattered over the sidewalk for the pigeons to eat. After he had gone inside the station I looked at where he had walked a long time, visualizing him lying there with his brains splattered at the bottom of the station stairs. It was not just him that I hated; it was all cops that I hated. They protected one another's misdeeds, and that made them all guilty in my eyes. The hate made me weak inside. It was destroying me, and I suppressed it, and I went out of my way to wave at them in their squad cars any place in the city I might be driving through or speak to them in a restaurant or post office. I could not function properly with that degree of hate in me. I only wanted one man dead while I was still breathing air on this earth.

"The next day he did not come to work, and I wondered about him. I knew that it could only be months at the most

To Kill a Cop

that he had, and at night I would drive my taxi to his neighborhood and sit outside far enough away to watch his abode and think about the sickness that was in him, the pain that was inside of him growing and eating away at the life that was in him.

"I again found myself becoming obsessed beyond control. I asked myself if I was a mad man. I went home and re-evaluated what I was doing and why I was doing it. I went over and over in my mind again the death that happened that night and could only see that man shooting without purpose, and I regained my potency and my purpose, and I continued on my path to kill that one man.

"I stayed at my post for my victim's return, but he did not return. One day, the woman who I had seen kissing him at his doorway came to the station, and I saw her walk up the stairs into the station. I locked and left my cart and followed her up the stairs into the station and pretended to use the telephone. I watched for her to return from one of the offices that were inside the station, and when she did not come from one of those offices, I placed money into the telephone over and over again and theatrically pretended that I spoke to more than one person during my hour there. Then, when I was almost through with my acting, I saw her come from the office of the station captain. With a small reticule held in both hands, dangling at her front thighs, she held her head so that her eyes looked down to the floor as she listened with sadness to the captain behind her.

"I found a reason to stay at the telephone longer, and I listened with one ear to find a place to intervene, and I did intervene. I stepped forward, and with a polite interjection I mentioned that I was indeed an acquaintance of her husband. I asked how he was at home, and she mentioned with a sad face that he was not well. My heart rose in me. I told her of my sorrow, and I offered her a box of my vegetarian cookies, and she refused them and my heart sank inside of me. Before I left her I asked again, and she refused. I walked back to my cart unhappy and worked with thoughts in my mind to finish that man with a bullet to his head.

"Whenever the sergeant did not come to work, I would pack my cart back onto my van and leave early. All was lost in my endeavors if I did not know for certain that the sergeant was dying. I would sit at night in my taxi and with a newspaper in front of my face, pretended to read and wait for a call from the radio. But I did not read or listen for a call over the radio but only peeped through holes in the newspaper I had made to watch the house my victim lived in. One morning I saw him come from his house with a cane in his hand humped over it like an old man making his way to their car as his wife locked the door to the house. He would not die, and the food I would sell him and the cookies that I would make him did not cause his demise fast enough, and he had not had any of those food products for some months. I made up my mind that I would drive up and blow his brains out in front of his house the next time he came out. I followed them in their car until I lost them along the streets of the city, and when I got home that night, my senses came back to me again, and I decided to wait it out until the plan I had started was complete.

"That morning, while lying in bed, I began to lose my patience again, and I started to think like a mad man. I wanted to finish him off. I wanted to shoot him with my father's pistol. But what I really needed was a rifle to reduce my chances of someone knowing who shot him. It had to be a stolen rifle, but I had no knowledge about rifles of any kind. I went to the library and took home some books about the subject, and bought some magazines about the matter, and studied until I knew what I wanted. I realized that the rifle I needed would have to be a high-powered one. I required a rifle that could explode a man's head from a mile away. I needed a perched position to place a bullet in the head of that man to escape capture, and as I drove around the neighborhood of that animal in my mind, I could not

To Kill a Cop

remember a building of that height being within a mile of his home.

"I had to steal a rifle to make sure that I was not discovered. I did not know where to steal a rifle, nor did I know of anyone who could steal one or sell one to me.

"I was in front of the station everyday selling my food products. I had never missed a day selling my products for fear that I would miss a day selling to my intended victim. Even though he had not come back to work for several months, I was there to hear word of his death or to observe his deteriorating health. He did not come to work and because his death would not come, I again had decided to blow his brains out at the cart and take my chance on the run from the law. One day he did come to work. He was not dead, and as he came towards my cart I waited for him to get close enough so that my aim would not fail me. After he had come close enough, I reached inside the compartment that I kept the pistol, and the pistol was not there. I did not search for the pistol in another place and only looked at the empty drawer where the pistol was always kept and remembered that I had taken it out before I had cleaned the cart and had not replaced it. A pain came over me as though a knife had been placed in me, and I leaned forward and placed my hands at my knees and moaned as people do who are suddenly overcome with some kind of illness.

"He asked me what the matter was with me, and I waited a moment and looked up at him through the sunglasses that hid my intentions, and a lie came out of my mouth that it was a sudden pain inside my abdomen that caused me to cry out as I did. I sighed and raised myself up to serve him and contemplated if I was quick enough or strong enough to take his gun from him to kill him and escape before the people around me could assist or call for help.

"I went home that night, and I set inside my room for many hours thinking about how close I was to destruction, how I could at that very time been on the run across the country from the law or dead with my body in the morgue.

159

Memoirs of a Taxi Driver

My life was in disarray, and I only lived to see that murderer dead, and I could not carry on that way to accomplish my vendetta against the man who had murdered my brother. But as I thought about how my brother had died and the bullet that had entered his skull, I came back to my senses, and my revenge became stronger again and I made my plans to continue.

"However, I knew that I could not continue as I had been. I made too many mistakes, I was not sure when the man would die, and he always recovered whenever he was away from my cart for a time. I was not a criminal, and I did not associate with criminals. I had never committed a homicide, and I did not know how to commit one other than the way I was doing it at the time. I was wrong for trying to kill that man. I would have to answer to God for my crime. I wanted to stop what I was doing. But again, I had a change of mind after thinking about it. I loved my only brother, and I was going to kill that dirty cop for murdering my brother. I needed a rifle, I needed to know how to fire it, and it had to be one that no one could trace to me. I contemplated stealing one, but I had no knowledge of where to steal one or whom to get to steal one for me. An idea came to me one day while I was looking through one of the many gun magazines that I had been purchasing. Gun stores had rifles and pistols. If I could burglarize a gun store, I could get not just one rifle but also all the ammunition I would need to learn to shot the rifle expertly from a great distance.

"Before I decided to burglarize a store, I decided that I would rent an apartment in one of the many apartment buildings that surrounded the police station to see how difficult it would be to rent one. I did do that, and when I found that there were ample apartments to be had for my purpose, I then started to search for a gun store in my area that I could burglarize. The stores that I selected were well protected with electronic burglar alarms and cameras. Not only that, I had no experience in burglarizing anything--as I mentioned to you, I was not an innate criminal, and it was

To Kill a Cop

very difficult for me. All the time that I was planning that crime, I was at my venue in front of the station everyday to give my victim his hot dogs, hot tamales and polish sausages. He became ill, as I knew he would, but his demise would not happen. After a few days away from me he would get better. It was a matter-of-time that he and everyone around him would put two and two together and discover that I was the reason for his illness.

"I made up my mind to burglarize a store in a neighboring state. I placed my hands on telephone books in every city and town in that state I could. I selected the towns that were far and near me and through conversations with my victim I found out when he would take his vacation. But luck was with me, and he became sick again. When I found that to be the case, I left immediately on my mission to find the gun shop that would be the most vulnerable to an amateur such as myself. While driving around I found some of those places were impossible to burglarize, others were easier. I found one store in a small town that was so easy I thought that it might be a trap for me.

"On the night that I had decided to burglarize my selected target, I stayed at a campsite in the forest outside of town. I thought very carefully about my endeavor, I thought that it was foolish and decided to leave. But again, my hate for my intended victim caused me to continue. After I had made up my mind, I came close to where I was to do my job, and a sense of reality came over me that I was being foolish in what I was doing. I became unnerved, and I went back to my campsite to lay myself down inside my tent to think about it all over again. After I had done that, I saw where I had no other choice but to do what I had planned, and I went back to my schedule to burglarize that establishment. I crept through the forest to the small village and observed it for a long time. From there I came close to my target, and after checking again as I had several days earlier, I broke through the barred window that had no electronic security protection as I had surmised. Through the shop to the rifles I

Memoirs of a Taxi Driver

went. I took two high-powered rifles and enough ammunition to last me a year. I wasted no time and escaped back through the window, back to the perimeter of the shop; back outside the village and to my campsite.

"I did not procrastinate in dismantling my campsite and entering my van to drive off, but it was impossible for me not to see two police cars sitting at the gravel road leading from my campsite, blocking my departure. My heart went to my throat, and I was told through a megaphone to stop the car and to step out with my hands in the air. I knew I was finished, and I did as they asked. I was taken to a larger town and placed in a jail cell for three days and sent to a county jail after that. That same night I saw a judge, and he placed my bail bond at an exorbitant amount that I did not have or my parents would not have with them after working all their lives.

"My parents knew I was on vacation, and they did not expect a call from me for at least a few days or a few weeks. The state told me if I pleaded guilty it could get me off with as little as nine months in jail but no more than two years. I knew I was guilty, the sheriff's police who had watched me secretly for three days knew I was guilty, so, to expedite my crime through the court system and because I had no money of any quantity, I took that offer that was given to me and I received fifteen months in jail for the burglary. I wrote my parents a letter without a return address and told them that I had found a job in another state working for the government and not to worry about me. I also told them that it was top-secret, that I could not talk about it, and I would not be calling them regularly. After about fourteen or fifteen months I would be finished with my assignment and be home again.

"I felt ashamed. I could not understand how I had come to the situation that I was in, but I was in that situation. I was in jail, and I was guilty. I swore to myself that I would never be so stupid again in my life, and I faced my time in that jail like a man. I could not blame anyone but myself. I

162

had lost everything I had worked for, but I knew that it could have been worse. I set there and decided that patience and a well thought out plan should have been paramount, and I had failed to adhere to that and let impatience overtake me. For thirteen months I was fettered in a dorm with other men, and after that time was served, I was on a bus back home.

"My parents were no problem. I lied to them as an adult-child, telling them that I could not talk about the job I had with the government, and they only settled down around me with their joy on my return. I settled down for a few days, and after I had reacquainted my thoughts with my original plan, I went back to the library and studied some books and decided to use cyanide to take my victim to his death. But I did not know were to find cyanide, when I did come by it I was afraid that it could be traced to me. My victim would have died immediately anyway, I would have been discovered.

"I changed my thinking on that and decided to either shoot him at close range one night as he would perhaps come home from some function or another. But there were problems with that: I could be seen possibly waiting for him outside his home before shooting him, I could possibly be seen while shooting him in the head, as I was planning, or I could be recognized even with a clandestine disguise.

"I thought carefully how I should continue and saw that there was no other alternative for me but to continue with my original plan, which was working, but not with the quickness I had hoped for, or to continue on with my original plan until I could figure out some other plan that would work for me to end his life.

"I borrowed some money from my parents to buy the products that I would need to restart my small business and prepared to resume my efforts when I got the most wonderful idea. I would make it seem like an accident. I would wait for him outside his home and run him down with the used van I had purchased. Of course it would be an

accident. 'I accidentally stepped on the accelerator, thinking
that it was the brake' or 'I lost control of the car' and
dragged him three hundred feet. I was so elated. I could not
sleep that night. The pain of my brother's murder was
expunged from me, and I drove home and completed my
chores without consciously knowing that I was doing them
or that I had even done them.

"I took a small vacation away from my planning and
examined every iota of it to make sure that I would not fail.
I then drove by his home, and then I drove by the station
where he worked. I felt very happy inside, and to confirm
my comprehension of the matter, I walked past his home
and the station at night to get the feel of my plan. When I
was sure of every intricacy of my plan, I borrowed my
mother's car to drive down the block at different hours of
the day and night and found that I would attract attention
and changed that practice and rented a taxi and did it that
way, and no attention was brought upon me. I worked
everyday in that manner, and I made sure that I only set
there while waiting for a call to come over my radio.
Whenever I got a call, I would take it and return to my place
to sit and wait for my victim.

"I waited for him in the morning to leave for work. But he
never exited at his usual time in the morning. I did that for
several mornings, and he did not exit. I went to his job, and
he did not arrive after I had come, and I assumed he was on
vacation, and I waited a week and resumed my observation.
When he still did not become visible to me on those
occasions, I feared that he had moved or divorced his wife
and moved away. Late one night after everyone had gone to
sleep, I quietly pulled my taxi in front of his house, tiptoed
to his front door and saw that his name was still on the front
door. I tiptoed back to my taxi and drove away knowing that
he had a shift change and decided to change my schedule
concomitant to the shift he would be working.

"I did that and found that his wife would leave out at a
certain time, but he never left. Something was wrong. There

could be no mistake, and I decided to reinstate my cart and stand out in front of the station to sell my food products and find his whereabouts in the city. After I had done that, I was received with raised eyebrows, smiles, and questions from my old customers about my absence for such a long time. I lied expertly, and I told who would ask that I had a vocation with the government that did not do well with me and had decided to resume my small business. My business was more profitable I told them, and I felt good about doing it. Whenever I was pressed for more information, I would only reveal that I did not want to talk about it because it brought back bad feeling to me, and that would stop the questions from them.

"I did not ask any questions about the man I would murder. I waited and watched with piercing eyes at the entranceway to the station, and he never came. One day I obliquely mentioned that I had been away a long time, and I missed the sergeant and wondered how he was doing to a lieutenant who ate a hot dog at my stand. He told me that the sergeant had died only a few weeks after I had stopped working in front of the station. When those words were spoken to me, my knees grew weak under me, and with no hint that my equanimity had been altered, I continued to listen to the explanation that was given to me. After the lieutenant had walked away from me, I could not stand at my feet and went to sit down on the ground not far from my cart. When people came to me and asked if there was something ill inside of me, I only raised my arm to shoo them away with a smile on my face.

"After that was done, and my customers had left, I went to the station and asked the lieutenant what it could have been that caused him to die so suddenly. I was told that the doctors did not know what it could have been. It was as though the life had been eaten out of him. It was heart failure or something of that kind I was told. Upon finding that out, I asked secretly of the others who had known him the best, and there was either no knowledge of the cause of

Memoirs of a Taxi Driver

his death or the same explanation as aforementioned was given to me.

"I went to my home that evening with my hands folded in happiness. However, I was not certain that he had died because of my efforts, and I had to be sure that it had been me that had caused his demise, and I finally decided to knock at the door of his wife to portray sorrow, and one Sunday afternoon that is exactly what I did.

"I forewarned her with a postcard that I would be coming, and when I did arrive on that date I had promised, I came with roses to make opaque my glee that he was dead, and I stood there at the door and explained to her further that I had sold food products from my cart to the people who might go to and fro about the neighborhood. She understood me and smiled and asked me to enter and to sit across from her as she touched and smelled the flowers that I had given her.

"I was not harsh with my desired interest but told her the falsehood that he was a wonderful person and that he was my best customer. She sadly moved her head up and down to acknowledge my condolences and said that it was the persona that he had tried to present to the world, but he was not a wonderful person and that he had killed innocent people before and gotten away with it because he was a licentiate in law enforcement and that he also was a wife batterer. I wondered why she was telling me that, and she told me that besides her family I was the only one she had told, because he would have killed her if she had told anyone or left him for any reason. She went on to tell me that she was sick and tired of people who worked with him telling her how good he was when she knew that he was not good and how anytime he got in bed with her it was hard to let him even touch her.

"She told me that she had been impregnated by him twice but had aborted the child each time because she did not want anything in her body from him. She went on as though I was a cathartic vehicle to reveal her dislike for that man

To Kill a Cop

she said that she had once thought she loved. It was a slow process that he had revealed to her that he had hit and shot a man in the face and planted a pistol on him to make his killing justifiable and shot a young boy in the back of the head as he ran from him and hit a pregnant woman in the stomach with his nightstick, causing her to lose her baby.

"I continued with my theatrical namby-pambyism, and I told her that she had to be mistaken. The man I knew could not have done such horrible things. She explained to me, sitting erect with her hands at her knees and looking down to the floor, that she had put it out of her mind for years, not wanting to believe that he was so cruel. But he was cruel. Whenever he got angry with her he reminded her he had shot and killed two men because they only did not do as he had told them to do, and he would shoot her if she did not do as he told her. And she did what he told her to do she told me.

"She pulled the sleeve of her blouse up to reveal a three inch scar and told me that he had thrown a steak knife at her and, before taking her to the hospital, had placed a gun in her mouth and told her if she said anything to anybody about what had happened he would put a bullet in it.

"She was a small woman. I looked across at her and told her how sorry I was, and I told her I did not know the truth until then. I thanked her and asked indirectly how such a young man could have died so young. She told me that it was some poison sickness that the doctors could not find in him that killed him. Something that ate away at him as an acid would eat away at anything it might touch."

The passenger's story was an interesting story to the taxi driver. The taxi driver drove on with the traffic to the airport. Ahead the traffic slowed at an imbroglio. There was silence in the taxi and both men made no effort to continue the conversation. Then the taxi driver spoke:

"So, so, are you leaving town?"

"I am leaving town. Forever. I am retired now. I am old now. Both my parents are dead now. I bought a small place

Memoirs of a Taxi Driver

in the Caribbean on one of those islands—I deserve it. I have worked hard all my life.

"Well, how did you do it? What kind of poison did you use to kill the guy?"

"I went to the grocery store. In the grocery store they have drain cleaner and other household cleaning products. I had to be very careful in measuring the chemicals. I used a modicum that the doctors could not detect. Mice are good to use as test subjects. I spent a fortune on mice testing those household chemicals, but it was worth it in the end."

The taxi driver drove on into the night to discharge the passenger. Not far in front of the taxi a police officer was directing the traffic at the airport terminal. The taxi driver slowed down to align his window with the officer directing traffic and starts to lower his window.

"What kind of work do you do besides driving a taxi?" the passenger asked.

"I only drive on Sundays. The rest of the time I am a police officer."

Boe, the Unveracious One

When it began, no one can know exactly. But they will tell you that those invaders came thousands of years ago from the north of the continent. They were a people from the Sudan who pushed themselves south with their iron tools to cultivate the land. After sometime, hundreds and a thousand years later, people from the outside of the continent came. Those people came from Asia, Europe, and other far off places in the world.

In the beginning, those people were tolerated. It was easier for the Zhun/twasi to accept those outside people than the warfare that would follow. In the end, after a thousand years of warfare with those people from the north, it was the people from Europe that brought the Zhun/twasi to near and total annihilation. There were raids on them; there was blood on the Zhun/twasi after they had come. With their bows and poison arrows, the Zhun/twasi found that they were no match for muskets, rifles, and automatic weapons.

Those people from the outside came in great numbers to the land, destroying not only villages close to them but also those villages far off and isolated from them. Along with those people from Europe, the Bakalahari, Tswanas, and

169

Memoirs of a Taxi Driver

Hereros, armed and mounted, came to rule the land and the Zhun/twasi.

So, long before a boy named Boe was born, some of the people left the traditional life they had lived before time was recorded, to work for the Hereros, Tswanas, and Europeans. They were herders for them, housekeepers, bearer boys, and in some instances the people would go off far to the south and work in the gold mines two miles deep in the earth.

But far off in the bush, invisible to the eyes of those from the outside, where the sand will not grow the crops of man, is were some Zhun/twasi managed to survive and lived the traditional life. It is there, outside a village is where Boe was born with his six-year-old sister standing there to acknowledge him. His father's name was Buks and his mother's name was Cha. They lived from the land that surrounded them, harvesting the plants and animals of nature.

In time, even they had to come in from the wilderness to live in camps established for the Zhun/twasi, with nothing to do all day. There were drugs and alcohol available to occupy the people from the boredom they suffered. Many took that route to legal and illegal substance abuse.

There was one that took another road other than crapulence, illegal substance abuse, failure, and destruction. When he left the land, he left with tears in his eyes. Gilded promises were made to love ones that he would not fail them. He would succeed; he would not forget his purpose he told them. Under the carapace of those gilded pledges, promises, he left a family and a girl that he would return to marry one day. On that morning, on a road unpaved, he left for the outside world. Across the desert quiet he flew, over the ocean current with its water deep he went, and when the bay of the Chesapeake came to his eyes, he saw its water and promise. Over the land to a city that was built on a prairie next to the shore of a lake he came to the earth. It is here, in this city that he has forgotten his tears, pledges, and

Boe, the Unveracious One

promises to his family and his love for the girl he would marry.

It is now seven years since his departure. He sits in a small one-bedroom apartment at a desk in a T-shirt and underwear. Behind him on the bed is a woman, soft as a girl in her youth. Her neck is long and slender. She complains unrelentingly to the man, and while complaining with her words, she appears to be conducting an orchestra with both hands in front of her enthusiastically.

"I love you Boe. Boe, I said that I loved you. Boe, why do you sit there and not respond when I tell you that? Don't you know how much I love you? I need you. Boe, I have told my parents about you."

The young woman raises herself from the bed and walks over to the man as he sits hunched over a desk with a textbook in front of him.

"Boe, Darling, I want to marry you. Boe, it is important that we get married. My parents don't know that I'm spending nights with you. Do you love me? Boe, you are everything in my life. I don't want to cry. Boe, don't make me cry.

She stoops down beside him and lowers her voice beseechingly, placing long slender fingers at his shoulder.

"Boe, have I done something to make you want to leave? Boe, please talk to me.

"Boe, I know that I am spoiled, spoiled by my father, my parents, but I promise you that I will be good to you. I will not abuse you or forsake you because of it. Do you think I'm a spoiled brat? Well, I'm not. Look at me Boe."

The man without removing his eyes from the book turns and benevolently places his lips at the woman's hand to kiss it. She is imploring him again. Even though he has told her hundreds of times not to while he is studying. He resumes his reading without discourse. The woman raises herself to stand behind the man and embraces him about the shoulders and then folds her hands tightly at his abdomen above his

Memoirs of a Taxi Driver

lap. He smells fresh to her, so clean and fresh. She kisses him at his right ear.

"Boe, I love you. Thank you for having chosen me. I am so proud to be with you Boe. I will be so good to you. I will never be mean to you, unkind to you. Boe, I want to have a child, I want lots of children, Boe. I want them to look like you. Boe, I will be so proud to have your children.

"Boe, we will have two or maybe three children and have a house in the country, and on Mother's Day you will bring me flowers and on Father's day I will buy you socks. On a warm summer's day, Little Boe will come to you and ask, 'Hey Dad, can I go out and play?' and you will say, 'Go ask your mother.' And at night, after the children have been put to bed, I will lie with you and tell you Little Jeannette helped me bake cookies that afternoon, and you will say, 'You should have told me, her cookies are almost as good as yours.' We will laugh together, you will hold me in your arms, I will hold you in my arms, and we will fall asleep together in love."

The young woman thinks for a moment, seeing those happy forebodings in front of her and waits for a response from the man and then looks down at him.

"Boe, you are so mean to me. Boe, I remember that day on campus when you walked up to me. The sun was over me, and the day could not have been better, and all of a sudden a large shadow came over me and would not move, and I looked up at you. I first noticed your pearly white teeth and your handsomeness behind those teeth. You were just standing there looking at me. I was trying to read Boe, and you were blocking my light. Oh, Boe, you were so handsome—I had never seen you on campus before. You are charming, aren't you? Aren't you charming Boe? Was I really beautiful? Was I the most beautiful girl on campus?

"Boe, I fell for every word you were telling me. Didn't I?

The man smiles and stretches to relieve the monotony that his muscles feel and places his raised arms behind the

172

Boe, the Unveracious One

woman's head and pulls her down over him to place a kiss at her lips.

"Jeannette, go look in the refrigerator. I bought some of those chocolate peanut clusters you like."

She bites his wrist and turns toward the refrigerator.

"Boe, you know I shouldn't be eating candy. You are going to make me fat."

He resumes his studying, thinking, concentrating over the textbook. The young woman returns chewing one peanut cluster in her mouth, while ingesting another with tiny bites. She sits at the edge of the bed on his left side looking at the peanut cluster in her hand before finally consuming it. She is a tall woman with a very thin waist and long athletic legs and thighs that fit perfectly in any skirt or dress. Her shoulders are narrow and feminine.

"Thank you for the candy.

"You are welcome Miss Wonderful."

"This summer my parents want to meet you. You have to come home with me. I can't understand why you are so afraid to meet my parents. They will not consume you. I love you. I want my parents to meet you.

"I have this feeling in my heart, if you leave you will never come back. Why must you leave now? This country is the place to be, not Africa. Do you know how many people want to come to this country? Every year people swim with the sharks to come to this country. We have the best hospitals, universities, and the best roads. We have everything here. That's why you are here Boe—we have the best of everything."

The woman sits for some moments without speaking, hoping for a response from the man. She looks at him sitting hunched over the textbook and admires his thick muscular thighs and calves. She pushes herself from the bed and walks over to him once again and kisses him and tugs at his shoulders requesting him to stop for some minutes to talk to her.

Memoirs of a Taxi Driver

"Boe, come here for just a minute. I only want a few minutes of your time. Please?"

"Wait. Let me finish this last page. One moment."

After a few minutes of concentrated effort at the pages in front of him, he pushes back the chair, stands and stretches on his tiptoes with his arms in the air, reaching for the ceiling and smiling at her.

"Oh Baby. I needed a rest anyway. If it were not for you, I would never stop. It is good to have a woman around."

"Boe, sit down on the bed for a minute. This is important."

Before sitting down on the bed in the small room, the man stretches once again as he did before, and the woman looks at him and thinks how she had to have him. He was the only male other than her father who understood her. She is determined not to let him leave out of her life.

"Boe, look at me. This is the only country, the only country in the world that you can be over weight, have indoor plumbing, wall-to-wall carpeting, a color television set in every room, air conditioning, a small saving account, a used car, and still be considered poor. There is no place on earth where that can come to fruition but in this country. Why, why do you want to go back to that jungle over there?"

"It is not a jungle. It is more like a desert."

"Joan, the African lady above you with the little girl, ask her about how hard it is in Africa. She used to live there. Now she lives here. Remember she told us that she worked in a restaurant at night, cleaning it up for the morning rush. Ask her way she is here, and she will tell you. She will tell you that it is better to clean a restaurant at night, have indoor plumbing, a used car, wall-to-wall carpeting, and a small saving account in this country than to live in the jungle."

The man looks at the woman. He smiles inside because she really doesn't know enough about Africa to comment. She is an absolutely glorious creature. She is intelligent. He

Boe, the Unveracious One

wonders why such a beautiful woman would want him? Does she know the significance of her beauty, he wonders? He has told her enough. What is admirable about her more than any other aspect of her physical presence, he surmises, is the opulence of her dark skin color and her short, kinky hair. It is soft and resilient. Her eyes are slightly slanted, clear and healthy. She smells clean and takes more than one bath a day on occasion. She is a very neat female, with very little wrong with her.

Inside of him is a burden that cannot let him rest, and he wonders in what way he may resolve it without hurting her.

"It is a desert. Not a jungle."

"Boe, there is something about Joan. One day you were taking the train to that three o'clock class. I saw you waiting for the train as I walked by the station, and I brought my face closer to the glass door of the station to make sure it was you. I saw Joan standing there behind you, just staring at you without your knowledge. You were just sitting there reading one of those textbooks, and she was just standing there, hidden by that partition, looking at you and some pain came over her, and I saw a tear come to her face. She turned and stepped back, in that way, when her face was completely turned in my direction is when I saw for sure that some emotion had come over her, and she stopped a tear from escaping from her eye. She seemed to regain her equanimity and turned to continue to stare at you until the train came.

"But what was bizarre indeed, was that she did not get on the train. She watched you get on, then wiped her eyes and came from the station. I stepped from her view as she turned, and I saw her walk back to the building with sadness on her face. Some past event must have come to her mind. You never know what cataclysmic events people have gone through in their lives. I have to find a way to ask her what that was all about--I adore her child though. She is so handsome, so black and shiny.

175

Memoirs of a Taxi Driver

"She told me she was Fulani. Is that true? Boe, if that woman is not of your ethnic group, why did I over hear you and her speaking together in the laundry room. I overheard you and her conversing in your language before I put the key in the door downstairs. When you and Joan saw me, you converted to English. Explain? Are you going to have an intimate relationship with that woman? Boe, I like her, but I am not going to have you in bed with her."

The young woman removes her shoes and places her feet in front of her on the bed, in the process, her skirt folds back to reveal white panties between her legs. She reaches forward with her right hand and pulls the man over to the bed in front of her. The young man takes her feet in his hands and massages them before she begins to speak.

"Boy, you are so, so, secretive. Why can't you relax around me? I am not going to control you. Do you think I am trying to take over your life Boe? I'm not trying to take over your life. I'm trying to love you. Why do you have to go back now? You are not coming back, are you? Boe, I know you are not coming back here. I will not let you go. I will refuse to let you depart on that plane."

The man reaches down and affectionately bites her toe and smiles upon raising his head. The woman grabs her stomach and leans forward.

"Jeannette you have to stop eating out at those restaurants. The food is making you sick."

"It's only the peanuts in the candy. I just can't seem to eat peanuts. The smell of them is starting to make me sick.

"Jeanette, I have something to admit to you. It is something I never thought I would have to admit to you. You are correct. You are right when you say that this country is the best in many ways, but I must return home. If I could in anyway avoid going back I would. I am happy here. I am happy with you.

"If you would have looked behind my suit case in the closet, you would have found some letters from my sister telling me that our father is sick and cannot see or hunt the

176

way he once did. My mother has to work for the both of them to make ends meet. I must return. My parents are not young as they once were, and my sister does not live in the village near them. In my sister's last letter I sensed that her marriage is not doing well and that her husband is drinking heavily. My presents and money would benefit them all. Those letters are from some years ago. Can you imagine how worse it as gotten? I have to go back and check on my people."

The woman makes sure that he has finished before interjecting.

"Have you been sending money?"

"No, I have not been sending money. Our postal service in my country is not reliable in that way, and even my sister's letters are not all here with me. It is better that I go there. It has been seven years, and I must return now that I have worked and studied in this country and have some funds for them and myself."

"Take me with you Boe. I can help you. If it is money that you need, I can help you. My family has money. Come meet them and you will see."

"No, no Jeanette, it is not that. Your money is not important to me. I have learned a lesson I think. Money and other priorities have kept me from my pledges and responsibilities. I feel shame. I feel ashamed of my behavior, my neglect.

"Also, it is not just my immediate family that is in turmoil, but my people in general. With my knowledge and education I can help them. To take you with me would be unfair to you. My country is not like it is here in this country, it is poor and dry, and it gets hot during the day and cold during the night, and indoor plumbing is far and in-between. Stay here. Stay in this country while I do my work with my people."

"What do you mean stay in this country? What am I suppose to do while you are gone? I'm not staying here man! I understand how important your family is to you. I will not stand in your way. Just let me go with you after I graduate next spring, Boe. Wait one year, and we shall leave together. Would it not be a good idea to stay here, find a job in finance, and send money home securely? Have you contemplated having your family come here to this country? My father is an attorney. My father can help. You have never talked to me about your family much. Why is it that you cannot trust me?"

The man places his hands in front of his face and yawns. Hoping that act would keep hidden from her other secret motives that has caused him to make plans to leave. He sits in front of the woman nodding his head up and down affirmatively, imploring with that behavior to find an avenue to interject. He raises a finger.

"That is something to think about Jeanette. Fortunately, I have been offered a job over there, and I do have some money. Remember, I have been driving that taxi for five years now. I am a frugal person when it comes to money. Look at this small apartment; it is not expensive at all. Furthermore, I should have some money after studying finance in college. If I have been studying finance for all these years and do not have any money after all those courses, I would, I should definitively be embarrassed."

"Boe, are you going to make love to a woman when you get over there?"

There is quiet in the small apartment, and a smile causes creases to form around the man's cheeks, culminating in deep long dimples there. He looks directly into the woman's face. He is discombobulated for only a solitary moment.

"Jeanette, how is your mind thinking? Help me with the workings of a woman's mind? What has motivated you to ask me questions about infidelity? I am going there because of my family. I have not seen them for seven years. They need me. They need help Jeanette. With the money I have saved, my family could live for years to come without working. American currency has great value in my country. My parents invested a lot of time in raising me, and I must

Boe, the Unveracious One

return to them. I have been irresponsible. I have been that way too long."

The woman stands up, and walks over to the window and looks down into the street as an elevated train pulls into the station. The people scramble into the doors of the train, and the young woman smiles to herself. The people remind her of cockroaches scrambling away into cracks and crevices to escape some predator.

The thought of him holding another woman concerns her. There is a pain inside her chest where her heart is with the thought of such an event. She walks over to the textbook that the man had been studying and looks down at a page, turning one page to examine the illustrations, but she is not cognizant of any illustrations or of her actions. She turns and sits back down on the edge of the bed. She places her palms at her face, turns to look over her left shoulder at him. Her eyes are clear, brown, straight, feral, and scintillating as those of a feline, and she speaks to him softly.

"You're lying, Boe. You're lying to me Boe. You are going there to your family. I know that. But you're going there in particular because of some woman in your past. Boe, don't lie to me. Boe, I don't want to cry. Boe, don't make me cry. Please Boe. Darling, is it another woman? Boe, I'm not a fool, you have never told me you loved me. Why haven't you ever told me you loved me? You hold me away at a distance with an invisible hand. I can only get so close to you, and then you push me away from you. I have known you for almost four years, Mr. Amuwu. I know that you are hiding from me your thoughts, your past, and your emotions. Mr. Amuwu, I'm a woman, I can feel when you are hiding something from me. I know you better than you know yourself, Mr. Amuwu. I know what you like and don't like. I know what moves you and does not move you! Listen to me Boe! Don't lie to me! You are going there also to rendezvous with a woman that you are still in love with!!"

179

Memoirs of a Taxi Driver

She walks over to the desk and pounds the desk with her fist, causing the textbook to rise up completely from its station to settle again at a different degree as she finishes her accusation.

"Jeanette—"

She stops him from speaking with one step toward him, grabbing his T-shirt in a clenched fist to hold it at his chin. Her face is next to his face, and she threatens him through her clenched teeth:

"Jungle boy, you listen to me right now! Don't you lie to me, I love you, and you are going to do as I say!"

Her eyes swell with tears, and, magically, one large warm tear rolls down her cheek to hang at her young lips for just a moment before falling.

"Jeanette, let me go for one moment; let me talk to you."

The woman releases him and walks away gracefully toward the bathroom for paper to wipe her eyes. The pink skirt and blouse she is wearing fits her perfectly, and she returns and sits down quickly and places her chin in her left palm as a little girl would who is agitated.

"Jeanette let me—."

"Boe, don't lie to me. I have been reading those old dated letters from Nauka for over two years. I searched this apartment until I found them. You keep them behind the refrigerator in a box. I almost gave up, but I was persistent and I found them. I know what you are going to do when you get there. You are going to hold her and kiss her first, and at night you are going to make love to her. I have tried everything in my power to make you forget about her. I knew I had time on my side, and I worked at it. I know I am wrong for what I have done. But you are the only guy I have ever really been in love with, and I can't take the chance that you will leave and never come back. I would rather die than let you make love to another woman. I would rather die! Die!"

Boe, the Unveracious One

Tears start down the woman's face, and suddenly she bursts into uncontrollable sobbing, placing her face in the palms of both hands, and she cries a long time.

The man lifts himself up from the bed with a stoic expression on his face, puts on his pants and shoes, walks over to the window, and looks down three stories onto the street. The woman continues to cry, and he stretches again from his tiptoes and places both palms of his hands at the small of his back and leans backwards and yawns. He turns and walks into the kitchen, turns the coffee maker on, watches for the light to glow, returns back to his desk to sit sideways in his chair and looks at the woman still sobbing on the bed.

"Jeanette, would you like some coffee?"

The woman continues to cry, and he stands up and goes to the refrigerator and takes out the bag of chocolate peanut clusters and sets them down beside her. He returns to the kitchen and in a few minutes pours two cups of coffee.

"Jeanette, look at me. Jeanette, Jeanette, look at me. I want to talk to you."

She raises her head, expertly avoiding the gold bracelets at her left wrist as she wipes away the tears with the back of her hand. He hands her a cup of coffee and before taking it, she wipes her eyes one final time with the tissue paper next to her she discarded earlier.

"Jeanette you have invaded my privacy."

"I know—."

"Just shut up for a few minutes Jeanette! Why do you always have to do the talking around here—Miss Perfect?? You have abused my trust and privacy! Let me say something! If I had done that to you I would hear about it for twenty years!!"

While holding the coffee in his left hand, the man places his forehead down into his right hand and massages it. His hope was to avoid a confrontation such as this one. He feels even more irresponsible. How did this happen he thinks to himself? It could be worse. She could know the real truth he thought.

The woman looks down into her coffee, and silence comes between the two people. The man sitting sideways massages his forehead again and straightens his body to speak away from the woman. He starts off softly, slowly:

"Let me explain to you something that I have never told anyone. I do not expect you to understand everything. If you understand some of it I would have done my job.

"I have decided to change my life. I am starting to abuse you. I have started to lie to you. If I start lying to you, I will have to keep lying to you. Jeanette, I want to be a role model to you. I do not just want to be a man that has an intimate relationship with you and moves on. I want you to think of me as honorable and fair to you.

"I was going to do this in a way that would not cause me to lie to you. I wanted to wait. But you have betrayed me by reading old letters, letters that are years old, and I have no other choice but to tell you the truth, and I do not know how to begin or how to start.

"I am from a people that consider themselves to be the real people in the world. My people believe that they are of true blood. They have always thought that way in my country."

The man takes a sip of coffee from the cup in his hand. Beads of sweat start to form at his forehead, and he takes his thumb and forefinger and captures some of it before it runs into his eyes.

"I am here with you now; I speak with you now; but my people are poor people in the world, and I was not born in a hospital as you were but under a tree into the world. Before my parents finally came in from the bush, we moved about the land and lived as my people had before my birth. I grew to understand the land and the animals that dwelled within its confines. My parents were defiant ones. They did not trust the government, but in time they did submit.

Boe, the Unveracious One

"During the dry season, when my family lived near a government settlement, they would let my sister and I study at the school that was there. But when the season became wet again, they would move away and take us from the school. Our lifestyle was doomed however, and gradually over the years, my parents moved ever closer to the settlements and secured jobs on the farms of the Tswana families. We did not live on the government settlement but on the land of a Tswana family not far away. For years my parents worked on the farm as my sister and I studied at our books. I was lucky, and after graduation was able to leave and come to this country to study at this university behind this building we sit in now, but my sister was not so lucky. She married and now has children and a husband to take care of.

"I did not come immediately to this country. There was a girl, a girl more beautiful than I had ever known a girl to be, a girl that I loved, but one that was married to another man. We had grown up together sparingly. During the seasons we would move about, and at times we saw one another. I knew of her well. I was aware she was attractive, but I was only a child then, my eyes did not care about that then. We would play and run about, but it was only when I was in my middle teens did I know for sure that I loved her. I wanted to marry her, but I did not grow up with the hunting skills that my father had acquired. I was in the bush only some of the time and in my books most of the time.

"As I have told you, my family had moved to the East and lived near a government settlement, but on the weekends I would travel through the bush to visit Nauka. It came that we knew our love would never end, no one could ever subjugate our love, no one could ever destroy our love, but in time, things changed. It could have been the job I had with the Europeans or the extra schoolwork, but in the end, we soon drifted apart.

"I was in Botswana, away from my family studying when the news traveled to me that Nauka had married a man much older than herself. And after some months it came to me that she was with a child, and when that time had passed, I heard that the child had come into the world healthy. I was not for sure, but I heard the man that she had married was not kind to her and beat her with his fist. That was not my concern, and a year later, after I had gone home to my parents and returned back to Botswana to graduate, I heard that she was with a second child and later that it too was healthy.

"After I had been graduated from school, I was not sure about what I wanted to do in the world, so, at twenty-years-old I went back to my parents on the farm of the Tswana family and worked there, talked and lived on.

"After some weeks with my family, I went with my father through the village that Nauka lived, on our way to my uncles' village. At first, I did not see her. I had indeed forgotten about her, as you know, time can change our thoughts, our emotions when we are apart. Our thoughts are not frequent of those we once knew and loved; our emotions are not hot or warm for the ones we once cared for.

"As we came nigh her place, I saw a woman sitting by the door of an unlatched hut with two children running about her. It was not even in my mind that woman could have been Nauka, but it was Nauka I saw as my legs brought me closer. Her eyes were delighted to see me, and my heart was excited to see her, and I set down next to her to talk about her life and family. As we talked, my eyes could not help but notice that her back was swollen, and I asked her how that could be, and she told me that her husband had beat her, that he had packed the things that they had together, and left for the village that his parents lived in. She was a girl with a tough heart, but it was then that the tears came from her.

"I asked her how it could be that he would leave her. She said to me that he was just through with her. In the beginning he would not leave her alone. He wanted to marry her. He was like a fox and was always there in pursuit of her until she finally said yes to marriage with her

Boe, the Unveracious One

parents' approval, even though she had been promised to another earlier. Then, one day, he did not want her. He just left her behind with hunger children, her words told me. She started to cry again, with tears that I had never seen her cry. Her body shock like the land around a volcano when the hot lava comes from inside it. She explained to me that she was happy that he had left. She said she hated him.

"He took all the blankets that she had bought with the money she had earned from a European woman that she worked for and a trunk that she had bought to keep them in. She cried and cried, and my father asked what kind of man would do that, and she said a man that had lost himself in beer and tobacco.

"One month before my father and I had arrived in her village, she said she had saved seven rands that she had earned and hidden them in a small box. He found the box and went to the Tswana settlement and bought tobacco and beer.

"She felt good that he had gone. As her tears came from her, she swore that she would not take him back, and my heart was soft for her. I realized that I still loved her, and that she, and especially myself, had let things drift between us. I placed my arm around her shoulder, and she was so tiny, so feminine. I told her I would not fail her; I swore I would not forsake her.

"She told my father and I that she was returning to her parents' village and that the walk would be a long one. We helped her to her parents' place a day and a half walk away. It was during that time that it was obvious that she was pregnant with her husband's third child. My father and I looked closely, and it was indeed the case.

"After our arrival, I decided to stay with Nauka and helped her build a hut next to her parents' hut. My father went on to the village of my uncle, and I stayed with her and helped care for her two small children. A few days later, after we had settled, I left with her father, and we hunted, and when we came back to the village, my father was waiting for me. He stayed the night, and the next morning I told him that I was going to stay with Nauka because her husband had left her, and she was pregnant and she needed me.

"The days turned into weeks and the weeks turned to months until her second daughter came into the world without life in its lungs. I did not leave Nauka. I fell more in love with her and her two remaining children with every passing day we were together. Nauka was warm to me; Nauka was kind to me. It was good to come home and have children reach out to me. They were not concern about worldly things. They were only concerned about play and things that went with play; they trusted me.

"I was really in love with Nauka. On the days that I would work, she would walk me to the road that our hut was near and talk for a while. Just before I would leave, she would place her elbows at my shoulders, not hugging me but still talking to me. She would tell me we should never let anything come between us again. I promised her with strong words. Nothing, no one would come between us I told her. We eventually moved to the Tswana village to be close to my parents and to my work.

"I had a part-time job at the government settlement assisting the teachers when Nauka's husband came back into her life. That evening when I returned home, Nauka told me that she had seen the tracks of her husband nearby, and she took me to them. I looked at them myself and asked her if she was sure. She was sure, and on our return he was sitting outside our hut. He told her that he wanted her to come back to him. Nauka refused him and reminded him of the child he had left her pregnant with and the blankets and the money he had stolen from her. She would not go back with him, and he tried to force her, that is when we got into a fistfight, and all the others came to separate us.

"I told that foolish man that he was a no-good husband. I asked him how it could be that he would steal the money that his wife earned and go buy tobacco and beer with it. I

Boe, the Unveracious One

told him that no man who was worth anything would ever leave his wife pregnant, without the rands she had earned and take the only blankets that she had for herself and children. I tried to hit him again, but my father stood between us.

"She refused him, and he went to the Tswana headman. The headman asked to see Nauka, and it was there in front of the headman that she told her story, and her husband had no defense. The headman asked that he and she go home to sleep on it. The next day, they went back just as the headman had asked, and Nauka was sure about how her heart felt, and the marriage was ended at that time

"The foolish man would not go away, and I found him time and again outside our hut, and we fought and fought until slowly he came to the realization that Nauka would not go back, and he soon disappeared.

"In my country, whenever you have a child, you must come to the realization that it may not live into adulthood. We do not have the best of everything in my country as you have here. Grocery stores are far and in between. Hospitals are rare, under staffed, and cost more money than we have. It was Nauka's oldest child, her only son that died first. My uncle came and tranced for him, but God took him away from us. Not a year later, her only daughter died, and we both cried and cried. My uncle really worked on both of them, and my mother and sister came to help. We cried when they died, and Nauka cried, cried and cried. I held her, and told her to cry. I told her to cry because she had to cry to get it all out of her. The children looked so much like her. She just cried and cried. For a long time Nauka and me were in mourning, but in time, things grew to be almost normal. We just lived and lived.

"It was my job that brought me the opportunity to come to the United States. I would still be in my country now if it had not been for one of the administrators at the school I worked at that informed me of a scholarship available to study in this country. I was happy in my country, but applied because I was offered the chance. One day, while at work, I found I had won the scholarship. It was a full scholarship. I was shocked. I was so shocked. I could feel the shock on my face at that time, and even though I could not see my face, I can see the shock on my face this minute.

"I told Nauka about it, but I also told her that it would divide us with an ocean. My mother, my father, my sister, they were all happy for me with their celebration, but I had decided not to take the scholarship. I told Nauka that I was going to marry her, have maybe one or two more children and live together until we were old people in our country. But she would not have my thoughts in her mind and insisted that I go. Not just for myself she said but for all of us. The education and the culminating income would be good for us all she shared. However, I still refused all invitation from her and my family to accept and leave.

"She was important to me, I was very content with her, and my immediate family was important. I told her it was because of my initial indulgence in my academic endeavors that caused us to become lost from one another, and I told her that I could neither do that action or even to entertain it in my thoughts.

"But after pressure from her and those around me, I finally left on the truck of a Herero for the city. The night before I was to depart for my years away from her and my family, we stayed together and celebrated my early morning departure and looked at one another for long periods of time and tried to hold back tears.

"That night in our hut, Nauka and me held one another close with tears coming from ourselves. I promised her that I would not stray from her. She said I was silly to tell that thing. She loved me. She knew I would be faithful to our love. However, I told her I would not lay down with another woman. I swore to it in front of her. She smiled, her eyes sparkling, and placed her ear next to my heart and held me without any words coming from her. She loved me. I was her hero she told me.

Boe, the Unveracious One

"That morning, when the truck came for me, we all waited, and we all cried. Nauka stood off behind our hut. She would not come from behind it. She had her hands folded in front of her like a little girl, and when I called to her she would not come and just stood there trembling with tears coming from her. I went and retrieved her and brought her to my departing place at the truck. I said, 'Do not be silly little girl. You will be my wife when I return.' She looked up at me with her eyes so wonderful and said, 'If you do not come back, my love for you will cause me to find you. You are in me. You are deep inside of me.' I told her I would come back.

"I departed with the driver, my eyes stayed on my family as they became smaller and disappeared over a ridge that materialize from the landscape.

"It was a slow process that had my mind change into its corruption. It was so slow that I did not even notice the changes. I cannot blame my behavior on you. My slide into unfaithfulness began before I met you. I was twenty-two-years old when I left my country, and I am seven years here in this country, and during that time I have not been true to Nauka as I had promised. I am ashamed of my actions and the time I have spent here. I once again let the books, the money, and the love that came out of my heart for you make me forget my promise to her and my family.

"As I have said, I promised Nauka that I would not forsake her. I would not destroy our love. But I did. I found no time to write Nauka. Nauka's English was not good English, and the schooling she had was not good schooling. So was it the same with my parents. Whenever they wrote me they would have to find those people that would write for them. My sister would write for my parents and for Nauka. But whenever that was not possible, Nauka would have to walk a day and a half to the settlement and ask one of the administrators or some other person with writing skills to write her thoughts down on paper, for she had moved back with her parents.

189

Memoirs of a Taxi Driver

"I received her correspondences, but I was living fast and high, and I could not always write. All of that was before I had met you, Jeanette. I could not always write her the way I wanted, and the way that I should have. In time I stopped corresponding with my family, I stopped writing Nauka. I was driving the taxi and studying. I wanted to write, but it was impossible with the corrupt thoughts in my mind and the beautiful women around me. I worked, and I saved. I slept and I studied. The scholarship money was good, but it was not enough for what I wanted to do. Three years passed away from me, and I had not written. It was as though a rug had been pulled from under me, and now it is seven years.

"Unbeknownst to me, Nauka had become pregnant with my daughter on my departure. Nauka was in love with me, and it had been two years since I had written. She knew nothing of the world or how it worked other than what she knew around her.

After the baby was born, and my letters did not come for some years, Nauka went back to the European woman for work. She saved her money until she had enough to move her about the continent.

The European woman moved to Windhoek and Nauka followed her there taking the baby with her. She worked there until she had saved enough money to rent a room from a Herero family. The Herero family had children that went to school and they taught my daughter to read some words. She placed my daughter in a school there but moved to the north coast of the continent when she had enough money, and in the night she went across the strait to escape to the Spanish coast. It was there that she was caught on the beach and placed in detention and sent back to the north coast of the continent. Alone, with little money, they lived on the street until a Muslim family provided for them, and it was because of them she regained her strength to try again for the Spanish coast.

"It was in the night that she went. And it was in the night that she succeeded and mingled with Muslims on the coast

Boe, the Unveracious One

that she had been informed of by her Muslim benefactors. There she learned to read and write some Spanish, and through deception she was able to come by plane to Mexico with my daughter and with her Spanish mistress who had power in the world outside of Europe.

There is a secret place along the border that she crossed without her mistress' knowledge, along with others with their backs hot with sweat, and from there she came to this city with my daughter. With Mexican protectorates she lived until she found a job and enroll my daughter in school here.

"It was through her persistence and the efforts of others that she found my address in this city, for I had moved several times around this neighborhood, and at night and during the day when she did not work, she would watch for me, when, one day, she saw me come from this building with you inside my arm close to me.

"Nauka is a kind woman, and not far from here at the grill she got a job at night cleaning it confines for the early morning rush that happens. It was one late evening that you and I sat at a table near a busing station in the restaurant that I saw a woman not completely exposed to me but hidden from me by a partition. I only saw her left side, only her left eye as it followed me as she lethargically cleaned about in that area behind that partition. I felt I knew that woman, and I could not follow you as you talked until, beyond belief, I knew not to be in me, an event that I knew not possible, I realized to whom that face partially hidden from me belonged. It was Nauka who stood there, and when she saw that I knew fully who she was to me, she stood out in the open with her hands folded in front of her like a little girl without her eyes moving away from me.

"She then continued her work with her eyes fully upon me, with a smile small and delightful at her lips.

"I took you back to your apartment in a rush and tried to explain to you with my first lie that I had forgotten something or another, and I went back in a hurry to find the

191

doors locked to the restaurant and the lights turned down as they are when a business is closed. I peeked through the door and lowered my body to look pass tables to find some human movement, and I saw some shadow in the back of the business and a woman with a mob working vigorously with it to complete her work. When I knew that she could see me, I tapped at the door until she raised herself to look at me standing there.

"She stopped her work and did not smile until she saw it was I who was there. She walked over to the door, pressed her cheek against the glass, and tears came from her eyes. I asked why she would not open the door. She told me that she was locked in for the night, and only in the morning would she be able to leave the premises.

"I stood there for some hours, and she told me what I have told you through the crevices that lay at the door that night, and I went home and went back to that place in the morning and brought her to her home in the basement of a tenement, where a baby sitter stayed the night with our child. It was an old place with cockroaches and other four-legged vermin, and it was through my efforts that I got her a decent apartment. She has asked no questions about you or mentioned you to me or told the child that I am her father. I did not keep our agreement. I am ashamed of myself. I was a bad role model, and I have decided to change my ways and take them back with me to my country and accept the job I have been offered by the American bank last year in my country."

The man stops and walks over to the window to finish his coffee. There is no perspiration at his forehead, but he checks with his hand. There is tension inside his mind. He massages the area above his eyes.

"Where does she live?"

There is no sound in the apartment. The man looks out the window and is aware of the people moving about the sidewalk and on the train platform, but he cannot place his eyes on any particular person. He places the coffee cup to his mouth and there is finally the sound of his lips against the plastic cup.

"Jeanette, I have not made love to her, but Joan, Joan is Nauka. The little girl is my daughter. She does not know it yet however. I am sorry Jeannette. I did not know that this could ever happen. I want to be a man. I want to stand up to my responsibilities. I owe her; and I owe the girl. I will not, and I am not going to lie and betray you. I feel better about this now that you know. I know that you are angry. You can hit me now to get the anger out."

There is quiet in the apartment once again. It is a heavy quiet. It would be like a thick cool cold fog on a coastal shoreline, abruptly moving about the landscape from the ocean currents, and it is only broken when the man places the coffee cup on the window seal and turns to place himself at one knee in front of the woman. Her face is unmarked with emotion of any kind. He places his large hands at her arms and while doing so, she is limp, and her head and shoulders are obsequious to his touch. He looks into her eyes and tries to solicit some cognizance of her thoughts. She only looks at him without her eyes blinking themselves. She then leans forward and places her forehead at his shoulder and wraps her arms around his neck. She places an affectionate kiss to his cheek and leans back against the headboard.

"I'm not going to hit you. It is not necessary. That night, after you brought me home, I followed you back to the restaurant. Your face told the whole story. Your eyes kept looking passed me as we spoke. I did not want you to know I knew that something was wrong. So I excused myself and went to the ladies room and saw that woman standing there that your eyes could not get enough of. I saw you standing outside the restaurant for hours talking through the crevices of the door. But I lost you in my car to her basement apartment. I never found out where she lived until later.

"I knew she was important to you, but not how much until three months later when you got her an apartment above

Memoirs of a Taxi Driver

you. I was not sure who she was to you until I heard you call her name in the laundry room. I only pretended to just arrive at the laundry room at that time. I had been standing there away from your view listening to both of you talk. It was not the first time I had listened to the conversations between the both of you. I could not understand the language, but both of you spoke as though there was a past between you. I wanted to find out what was going on between you people. I finally found out when I heard you use the name in the letters while addressing her.

"I am in love with you. I did not want to loss you, so I wanted to play my cards right. There were many times I wanted to slap you in your face.

"I had to become friends with her to keep her away from you. That's why I invited them to the zoo, museums, and out to lunch. If she is with me, she is not with you. She is kind Boe. I find her compatible. I love the girl, and she looks like you, but I cannot give you up. I would be sad. I would not be able to explain my situation to my family, and I don't want us to live without you in our lives."

There is quiet in the room, the woman does not continue, and she places her hand at her stomach, leans the back of her head against the headboard and closes her eyes, making her eyeshadow cognizant for the first time to him.

"I can only live with one of you Jeannette. I do love you. But I have her, my daughter and my family waiting for me over there. I must go after graduation."

"No, Boe. You don't understand. Four months ago, before all this happened is when I found out that I was pregnant. Don't make any gilded promises or pledges. Come here. Hold my hand."

Speaking Engagements

Mr. Patterson is a public speaker and will speak in front of your group or convention on the following subjects:

1. How to avoid legal and illegal substance abuse.

2. How to live a life with very few problems.

3. How to become a master salesperson.

The author can be contacted at:

Trueblood Publishing
P.O. Box 806303
Chicago, IL. 60680

For an original autographed photograph of the cover, send
$19.95 to:

Trueblood Publishing
P.O. Box 806303
Chicago, IL. 60680

For a copy of "Memoirs of a Taxi Driver," ask for a copy at your local bookstore. If that is not possible, send $24.95 to:

Trueblood Publishing
P.O. Box 806303
Chicago, IL. 60680